BIOPHYSICS OF THE EAR

Publication Number 547

AMERICAN LECTURE SERIES

A Monograph in

The BANNERSTONE DIVISION *of*
AMERICAN LECTURES IN
BIOCHEMISTRY AND BIOPHYSICS

Edited by

W. BLADERGROEN, Jr., M.A., Ph.D.

Sandoz Ltd.
Basle, Switzerland

BIOPHYSICS
OF THE
EAR

By

F. L. DITTRICH, Ph.D.

Physicist of the Otological Department
Faculty of Medicine
University of Geneva
Geneva, Switzerland

In Collaboration With

R. C. EXTERMANN, Ph.D. h.c.

Professor of Experimental Physics
Faculty of Science
University of Geneva
Geneva, Switzerland

With a Preface By

G. F. Greiner, M.D.

Professor of Otolaryngology
Faculty of Medicine
University of Strasbourg
Strasbourg, France

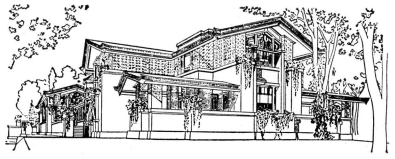

CHARLES C THOMAS • **PUBLISHER**

Springfield • *Illinois* • *U.S.A.*

Published and Distributed Throughout the World by
CHARLES C THOMAS • PUBLISHER
Bannerstone House
301-327 East Lawrence Avenue, Springfield, Illinois, U.S.A.

*With THOMAS BOOKS careful attention is given to all details of
manufacturing and design. It is the Publisher's desire to present books
that are satisfactory as to their physical qualities and artistic possibilities
and appropriate for their particular use. THOMAS BOOKS will be true
to those laws of quality that assure a good name and good will.*

Printed in the United States of America
D-10

This monograph is dedicated to
Professor Georg von Bekesy, Nobel Prize winner,
for his remarkable work in Otophysics

PREFACE

Doctor Dittrich's monograph on *The Biophysics of the Ear* holds many rewards for the thoughtful reader. The study of biophysical elements of the ear is an actual preoccupation. Such a work, that Doctor Dittrich has asked us to preface, corresponds to the present tendencies in otology which utilize the most recent data of experimental research in order to apply these to diagnosis and treatment of the ear diseases.

It is not necessary to present Doctor Dittrich. His formation, at the same time scientific and medical, predestinates him to write a synthetic monograph. Doctor Dittrich, physicist and physician, is capable to explain the physical principles and, on the other hand, his medical experience—as collaborator of Professor A. Montandon at the University of Geneva—gives him the necessary complements to understand audiology and to be familiarized with the problems of the vestibular apparatus to which the Geneva School of Labyrinthology has consecrated itself.

The chapters concerning technics and results present the essential part of Dittrich's monograph. He shows his spirit of precision and permits the opening of fruitful discussions and new deductions about physiopathology.

It is not possible to summarize in a short preface the whole work, pointing out the present state and the future perspectives of the knowledge in this field rich in considerations.

I hope that the biophysical vocation of Doctor Dittrich will stimulate him to produce more studies of this quality. I am convinced that this book will find its place in the library of all the otologists and physiologists; everybody will receive an answer to his desired information.

I wish to Doctor Dittrich's monograph the success which it deserves.

G. F. GREINER
Professor of Otolaryngology
in the Faculty of Medicine
University of Strasbourg
Strasbourg, France

ACKNOWLEDGMENTS

OUR GRATITUDE is especially due to Professor A. Montandon, of the Faculty of Medicine, University of Geneva, by whom we have been stimulated and encouraged in lengthy but fruitful discussions. He took pains to urge us to greater clarity in presenting a picture of our concept, especially in his insistence that we illustrate our ideas with suitable graphs.

Doctor R. C. Extermann, Professor of Experimental Physics at the University of Geneva, who has contributed to the redaction of parts of the second section of this volume, will find herein the profound expression of our gratitude.

Mr. J. Dreyfus-Graf, who has partly constructed his remarkable *"Phonetograph"* in our laboratories, has been an excellent collaborator for the establishment of new cochleo-vestibular cybernetics. To him we extend our warmest thanks.

Finally, Professor G. F. Greiner in writing the Preface to this monograph has demonstrated his warm sympathy toward our work.

The scientific literature has not yet produced a work treating the delicate problem of the Biophysics of the ear in a precise way. We wanted to fill this lack. We owe the materialization of this wish to Doctor W. Bladergroen, of Sandoz Ltd., Basle, Switzerland, who agreed to include this monograph in the series of American Lectures in Biochemistry and Biophysics published by Charles C Thomas, Publisher. May he find here the expression of our deep gratitude.

F. L. DITTRICH
Physicist at the Otological Department
Faculty of Medicine
University of Geneva
Geneva, Switzerland

CONTENTS

SECTION FOUR

ELEMENTS OF COCHLEO-VESTIBULAR CYBERNETICS

BIOPHYSICS OF THE EAR

SECTION ONE

INTRODUCTION TO THE BIOPHYSICS
OF THE EAR

INTRODUCTION

To THE KNOWLEDGEABLE and informed reader it may well seem presumptuous to attempt the exposition of the whole of such a complex subject in such a modest amount of space as this book contains.

It is understandable, however, at a time when the two compartments of the ear are called on to play such a great role, due to the ever increasing and more and more specific soliciting of their intimate functions, that one should wish to reunite the fragmented observations on a subject which yields only with difficulty to a synthesis. Such an attempt carries with it implicitly the risk of a certain inconsistency of exposition on a subject whose sources are distributed even less in space than in time.

The principal reason for the existence of this volume lies in the fact that the ear appears to be an organ essentially predestined to be the object of biophysical study. It is striking, in fact, to note how rare, in the animal and human economy, are the organs for which functional study has never separated these two sciences—Physics and Biology—which include one another.

The logical conclusion of this associative quality would seem to be the integration of experimental facts acquired to date in the cybernetic cochleo-vestibular circuit which proceeds from them. It is with this conclusion in mind that we attempt to justify the appearance of this monograph which without it would lack in originality.

The contents of this book, divided into sections in accordance with the purpose described above, can be summarized as follows:

A first section, introductive, in which the subject is placed in its anatomo-physiological and historical context.

A second section consecrated to the Biophysics of hearing.

A third section consecrated to the vestibular Biophysics or of orientation.

A fourth section, where the fundamental elements of a cochleo-vestibular cybernetics necessary to the intelligibility of the described functions and the interpretation of phenomena are reunited.

A great number of these phenomena are, as yet, to be discovered.

ANATOMY

THE GENERAL STRUCTURE of the ear must be regarded as a tripartite entity within which are found the organs of hearing and of orientation (Fig. 1).

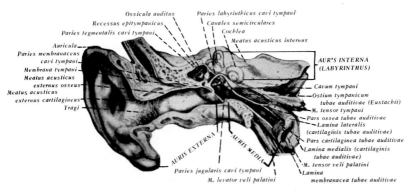

FIG. 1. The three parts of the ear (according to Woerdeman).

These three parts, which undertake very different functions, are: the external ear, which receives sound and measures the direction of the ondulatory field; the middle ear, the wind passage which transmits longitudinal sound vibrations; the internal ear, which analyzes and transduces the mechanical, wave-formed adequate stimulus to each of its compartments.

The various folds of the external ear contribute effectively towards the direction of sound waves towards the external auditive canal, a concave passage placed behind and below it, and towards the tympanic membrane. The external ear, in the form of a conch, consists of an exterior fold, the *helix*, which is continued forward by the *tragus* of the canal; the *anthelix* is itself concentric. Its upper section is divided into two branches by the *scrobiculus scaphoideus* and prolonged below by the projection of the *antitragus*. The external ear is attached to the skull by three muscles, atrophied in man, but which give animals an extremely great precision in auditive orientation.

The volume of air enclosed in the canal and the first recesses of the external ear is about 4 cc. The length of the canal, one third of which is formed by a cartilaginous part and two thirds by a profoundly osseous part, is about 25 mm; its diameter varies from 4 to 10 mm, according to the individual. The cartilaginous third part of the auditive canal is covered with thick, hairless skin, and glands that secrete an unctuous yellowish substance, the *cerumen,* formed for the most part of lipidics and proteics constituants.

The middle ear consists essentially of a group of air cavities containing the *ossicles* and their muscles (Fig. 2). Farthest back

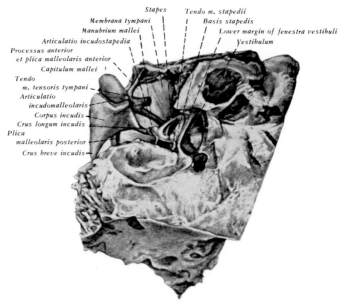

FIG. 2. The relationship between tympanic membrane and ossicles (according to Woerdeman).

one finds the *processus mastoideus,* which corresponds externally with the retro-auricular part of the skull exempt of hair; this excrescence has the purpose of maintaining the constancy of temperature, pressure and hygrometric degree. Internally, the processus mastoideus has connection with the *lateral sinus;* anteriorly with the *facial nerve* and above with the *dura mater.*

The *cavum tympani* has the form of a biconcave lens. As for the *membrana tympani* which closes the ear to the outside, it is thin, transparent and elastic, though at the same time very resistant due to its pluristratified structure of intercrossed fibers; tightly stretched on an osseous frame, it has a flaccid segment in its upper section. Although it consists of four layers of tissue, the tympanic membrane has a thickness of only approximately 1/10 mm in which the blood vessels and nerve fibers (these latter originating from the *nervus vagus* and the *nervus auriculotemporalis*) are distributed. The tympanic membrane is, moreover, attached to the most external of the *ossicles,* the *malleus.* The *caput mallei* is separated from the *manubrium mallei* by a contracted part, the *collum mallei.* The axis of the caput mallei forms with the axis of the manubrium mallei an angle of 140°. The length of the bone is about 8 mm, 3 of which form the caput, 1 the collum and 4 the manubrium. The manubrium mallei is incorporated in the thickness of the tympanic membrane, whose movements, consequently, it follows. The *incus* which articulates with the caput mallei is formed by two branches perpendicular to one another, of which one is directed downward, parallel to the manubrium mallei and joins, at the point of articulation, the *os lenticularis,* the smallest in the human body. It articulates with the round head of the stapes, whose name eliminates the need for description. The platform of the stapes frames itself in an oval space which it seals hermetically by means of a circular ligament. The ossicles are articulated by two powerful muscles: one, which inserts into the malleus, the *musculus tensor tympani,* it pulls the malleus, and therefore the tympan, downward;—the other, inserted in the stapes, the *musculus stapedius,* pulls that ossicle backward (Fig. 3).

On the anterior part of the periphery of the cavum tympani the auricular orifice of the *Eustachian tube* can be found. This canal is 35 to 40 mm long, and opens into the pharynx, above the *velum palati.* At its most narrow section this canal measures only 1-2 mm. in diameter. The osseous part opposite the tympanic mem-

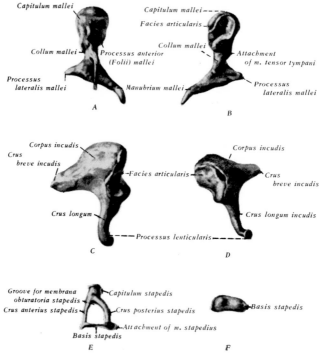

FIG. 3. The ossicles (according to Woerdeman).

brane presents two orifices: the *fenestra vestibuli aut ovalis* above, closed by the platform of the stapes and, below and behind, the *fenestra cochleae aut rotunda* closed by a membrane called the secondary tympanum. It should be noted that the entire cavum tympani is covered with a mucous membrane which is the continuation of that in the pharynx and the Eustachian tube. Inside the two fenestrae are the constitutive elements of the internal ear, the structure of which is very complex (Fig. 4).

A membranous sack, the *labyrinth*, following the form of its osseous matrix, and, filled with a fluid called *endolymph*, is suspended in another liquid: the *perilymph* (Fig. 5). Two parts are distinguishable in the labyrinth: the posterior and the anterior, with a very narrow canal, the *ductus reuniens*, communicating between them. The posterior labyrinth, seat of the organs of orientation, is made up of *semicircular canals*, the *utriculus* and

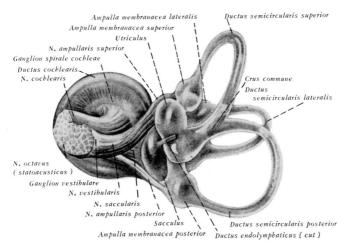

Ampulla membranacea lateralis
Ampulla membranacea superior
Utriculus
N. ampullaris superior
Ganglion spirale cochleae
Ductus cochlearis
N. cochlearis
Ductus semicircularis superior
Crus commune
Ductus semicircularis lateralis
N. octavus (statoacusticus)
Ganglion vestibulare
N. vestibularis
N. saccularis
N. ampullaris posterior
Sacculus
Ampulla membranacea posterior
Ductus semicircularis posterior
Ductus endolymphaticus (cut)

FIG. 4. Right membranous labyrinth (according to Spalteholz, enlarged 6.25 x).

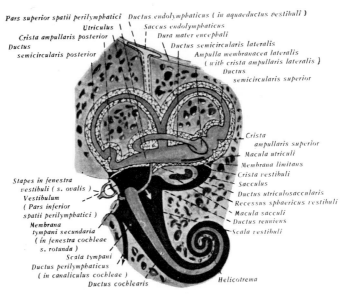

Pars superior spatii perilymphatici
Utriculus
Crista ampullaris posterior
Ductus semicircularis posterior
Ductus endolymphaticus (in aquaeductus vestibuli)
Saccus endolymphaticus
Dura mater encephali
Ductus semicircularis lateralis
Ampulla membranacea lateralis (with crista ampullaris lateralis)
Ductus semicircularis superior
Crista ampullaris superior
Macula utriculi
Membrana limitans
Crista vestibuli
Sacculus
Ductus utriculosaccularis
Recessus sphaericus vestibuli
Macula sacculi
Ductus reuniens
Scala vestibuli
Stapes in fenestra vestibuli (s. ovalis)
Vestibulum (Pars inferior spatii perilymphatici)
Membrana tympani secundaria (in fenestra cochleae s. rotunda)
Scala tympani
Ductus perilymphaticus (in canaliculus cochleae)
Ductus cochlearis
Helicotrema

FIG. 5. Membranous labyrinth and perilymphatic space (according to Woerdeman).

the *saculus;* the anterior labyrinth is coiled and for this reason is called the *cochlea;* the acoustic function is delegated to this organ. The semicircular canals are so placed that the upper canal describes a vertical arc from front to back; the lower canal a vertical and transversal arc; the horizontal canal is in a horizontal position with its curve directed from front to back. The five apertures of these three half-circles (two of the canals fuse at one of their extremities) come into communication in the utriculus and present three enlarged extremities (one for each canal), the *ampulla* in which the sensorial termination of the vestibulary nerve, the *cupula ampullaris,* is found (Fig. 8).

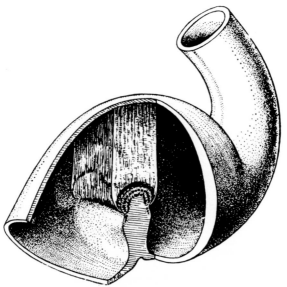

Fig. 8. Schema showing the situation of the cupula in the ampulla of a semicircular canal (according to Werner).

The membranous sac of the internal ear is completely closed and has no communication with the interior. On the contrary, the liquid in which it is immerged communicates with the *cerebrospinal fluid* by means of a miniscule canal: the *ductus perilymphaticus.*

The coiled tube which constitutes the cochlea is subdivided into two tiers or ramps by a semiosseous, semimembranous lamina which stretches from the base to the summit without completely rejoining the latter: this is the *lamina spiralis*. The free space remaining at the summit is the *helicotrema*. The upper ramp of the cochlea is the *scala vestibuli* which ends near the fenestra ovalis. The lower level is the *scala tympani* which terminates at the fenestra rotunda.

It is in the scala vestibuli that the membranous canal which contains the sensorial organ, called the *ductus cochlearis,* is found. It rests upon the lamina spiralis which separates it from the scala tympani; the membrane which separates the ductus cochlearis from the scala vestibuli is called the *membrana vestibularis Reissneri* (Fig. 7).

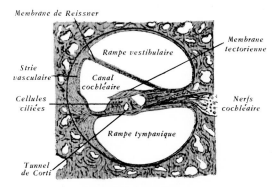

FIG. 7. Cross-section of the cochlea with the organon spirale (according to Collin).

membrane de Reissner = membrana vestibularis Reissneri.
membrane tectorienne = membrana tectoria.
Rampe vestibulaire = scala vestibuli.
Rampe tympanique = scala tympani.
canal cochleaire = ductus cochlearis.
strie vasculaire = stria vascularis.
cellules ciliees = ciliated cells.
tunnel de Corti = tunnel of Corti's organ.
nerfs cochleaires = nervi cochleares.

The sensorial organ which transforms sound waves into physiological phenomena is situated in the interior of the ductus cochlearis; the entirety of the cells of this organ is referred to by the name *organon spirale vel Corti.* The most remarkable part is formed of a series of arcades which together form a tunnel. Each arcade is formed of 6,000 external pillars and 4,500 internal pillars; the *arcus spirale* reposes upon the *lamina spiralis membranacea,* outside and inside of which the *ciliated cells* constitute the sensorial organ of hearing. There are about 20,000 external ciliated cells for 3,500 internal. In their upper portion the ciliated cells traverse a cuticle which allows only the cilia to appear. The cilia are in contact with a thick membrane to which they are attached: the *membrana tectoria.* From the base to the summit of the cochlea the diameter of the ductus cochlearis, the dimension of the arcus spirale, and the width of the lamina spiralis membranacea all gradually increase.

Lastly, it is around these ciliated cells that the endings of the auditive nerve open out (Fig. 6).

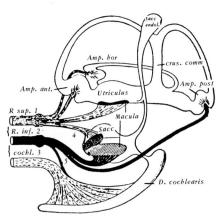

FIG. 6. Innervation of labyrinth (according to Burlet).

It is surprising to note that at a time when at least each month one or more new hypotheses relative to the physico-physiology of the vestibular apparatus comes into being, the anatomical data furnished by manuals, monographs and review articles are extremely rare. This is just the contrary of what occurs in the domain of the anterior labyrinth where every well-grounded graduate knows the principal structural elements. This fact should not be thought of as being a certain modesty on the part of authors who deem it sufficient to refer readers to "classical" sources since, of course, the anatomic basis upon which the physiology and the biophysics of the posterior labyrinth are built have all been known for a great many years; in reality, this silence constitutes one of the better illustrations of those forgotten words of Claude Bernard, well worth quoting here:

> "If a physician believes that his reasonings have the same value as those of a mathematician, he will be in the greatest of errors and will be led into the falsest of conclusions. This is, unfortunately, what has happened and still happens to men I would call systematic thinkers. These men start off with an idea which is more or less founded on observation and which they regard as an absolute truth. They then reason logically and without experiment, and, going from conclusion to conclusion, succeed in constructing a system which is logical but which has no scientific reality. Often persons of superficial intelligence allow themselves to be misled by this appearance of logic, and thus it is that in our days discussions sometimes occur that are worthy of ancient scholasticism."

It is of prime importance to make no mistake as to the role of comparative anatomy, first an aid to comparative physiology and then to physiology itself: in a word one must not confuse a semblance of analogy with functional identity as certain authors have done:

"Despite the distance in the animal scale separating the amphibian labyrinth and the human labyrinth, one finds, very clearly, certain anatomic dispositions and, unquestionably, a physiological mechanism which is strongly comparable to that which exists in man." (Ledoux.)

The recent and remarkable work of Rauch, Ferreri and Crifo (and in a lesser measure those of Dohlman), added to the classical data furnished by Witmaak and Werner, furnishes a vast enough documentation of the normal anatomy of the vestibular labyrinth, that there is no further need for confirming or invalidating this data with other data gathered in the "animal scale."

Numerous authors (principally Coassolo, Bairati, Belanger, Borghesan, Wersaell) have undertaken to describe the microscopic infrastructure of the normal vestibular receptor (Fig. 10). The greater part of their data is, nevertheless, still insufficient for the constituting of a model of ampulla exempt of approximations. In the same way, work undertaken by the pathologists is not more capable of enlightening us in regard to the precise knowledge of

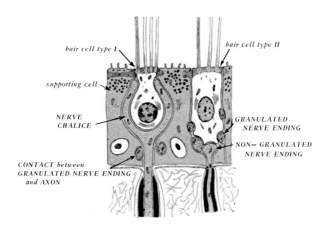

hair cell type I

hair cell type II

supporting cell

NERVE
CHALICE

GRANULATED
NERVE ENDING

NON– GRANULATED
NERVE ENDING

CONTACT between
GRANULATED NERVE ENDING
and AXON

FIG. 10. Schematic drawing of the innervation of the hair cells in the vestibular sensory epithelium as it appears in cat, guinea pig, and rat (according to Wersaell).

the degenerative processes proper to each type of structure as well as the interpretation allowed one according to the method of fixation used.

Rauch, working in Geneva, has obtained numerous histological sections of the normal posterior labyrinth in man, by his ingenious process of postmortem fixation at low temperatures. Nevertheless, the essential part of the work which he devoted to this subject had as its purpose the determination with greater precision of certain biochemical agents of the endolymphatic circuit.

It is thus to Professors Ferreri and Crifo of Rome that we owe a very great progress in our knowledge. Their microscopic studies have for the most part dealt with the elements of the membranous labyrinth in samples taken from Ménière's disease by the Cawthorne operation.

One of the first points that must be established is the opposite *fixation* of the cupula ampullaris. Several authors have attempted to demonstrate that the transformation of mechanical sensorial information into physiological phenomena was due, at this level, to a movement of the cupula in the ampulla, movement that they qualified as *pendular*. These facts, unfortunately, do not rest on a reality as easy to interpret. Steinhausen, to whom one refers invariably on this question, has never himself put forward this "natural movement"; on the contrary, one can see in the filmed sequences he has devoted to this subject, lateral *deformations* of the cupula between these two attachment points. Parallel to this *in vivo* argument, we can point out the *in vitro* one which shows, in all the histological fixations of this part of the semi-circular canal, a retraction of the cupular gelatinous mass

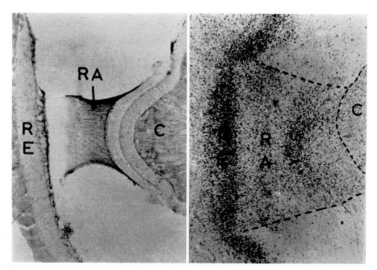

FIG. 9. *Left:* Midaxial section of the crista acoustica and adjacent structures from a three-week-old chick; 12μ celloidin section, stained by Hale's iron adsorption method and counterstained PAS. RE, roof epithelium; RA, roof appendage; C, crista.

Right: Unstained integrated S^{35} autoradiograph from the ampullar organ six hours after tracer administration to a three-week-old chick. From left to right: roof epithelium, roof appendage and epithelium of crista (C). RE, roof epithelium; RA, roof appendage. (According to Belanger.)

accompanied by a pulling away of endolymphatic tissue; this fact
postulates the opposite fixation, for if the cupula did not adhere
to the opposite wall, it would retract freely without carrying
along that wall. It is interesting to note, in this connection, that
the same error was made in the past in relation to the cochlea,
where it was believed that the membrana tectoria was "floating"
(Fig. 9).

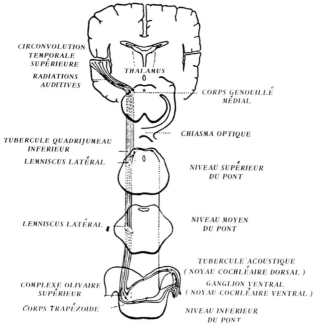

FIG. 11. The auditive ducts (according to Fulton).
circonvolution temporale superieure = gyrus temporalis superior.
radiations auditives = radiatio acustica.
tubercule quadrijumeau inferieur = corp. quadrig. infer.
complexe olivaire superieur = nucleus olivaris accessorius superior.
corps trapezoide = corpus trapezoideum.
corps genouille medial = corpus geniculatum mediale.
chiasma optique = chiasma opticum.
niveau superieur du Pont (moyen, inferieur) = pars superior (media,
    inferior) pontis Varoli.
tubercule acoustique = nucleus cochlearis posterior.
ganglion ventral = nucleus cochlearis anterior.

To the arguments furnished by histology can be added those of histochemistry. It is known that the distribution of the mucopolyssaccharidis acids of noncalcified bone and of cartilage is very positive. The same thing is true, in the anterior labyrinth, for the membrana tectoria and, in the posterior labyrinth, for the cupulae ampullares and for the otolithic layer of the maculae.

This chapter would not be complete without a summary of the ducts and nerve centers corresponding to the receptors described above.

For *hearing* (Fig. 11), the ciliated cells of the organon spirale articulate with the *first acoustical neuron;* the cells of this latter form the *ganglion spirale cochleae,* situated in the osseous cochlea. The *afferent fibers* of the *acoustical nerve* come together in the trunk of the acoustical nerve [VIII] which joins with the vestibular nerve [VIII]. Together they cross the [VII] (facial), then, having crossed the angulus pontocerebellosus, reach the two equilateralacoustic nuclei of the medulla oblongata (Fig. 12). The acoustical nerve, entirely composed of long fibers of the first

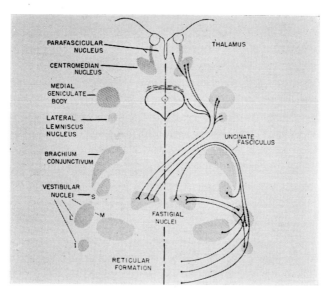

Fig. 12. Schema of the tecto- and vestibulocerebellous connections (according to Fulton).

neuron, has thus a radicular significance; it contains as well a small contingent of *efferent fibers* (Racine and Portmann) which are of a vegetative nature. The vestibular acoustic nuclei, from whence originates the *second neuron,* rise in one homolateral passage and another contralateral passage, by the lemnisci lateralis and medialis, up to the posterior corpora quadrigemina to the corpus geniculatum mediale and to the cortical area of Heschl at the level of each of the temporal lobes. In the course of this long passage in the cerebral trunk and in the central nuclei, the acoustical ducts of each ear are split, bilateral and quite separated. They are thus more or less inaccessible to massive lesions, except at their entry into the medulla oblongata at the level of the corpora quadrigemina.

For *orientation,* we know that there are two types of receptors:

1). the *receptors of movement,* which are constituted by the semicircular canals.

2.) the *receptors of position,* constituted by the otolithic maculae of the utriculus and the sacculus. These two appendices are equipped with an otolith, a kind of small chalk crystal attached to a sensorial zone: the macula.

The *afferent fibers* of the vestibular nerve issuing from the cristae ampullares come together in two fasciculi until the *ganglion vestibulare inferius* (Scarpae) situated at the bottom of the internal auditive conduit. They then form the VIII vestibular nerve which follows the same passage as its acoustical counterpart until the medullae oblongatae nuclei. Like the acoustical nerve, the vestibular represents the *first vestibular neuron* and has the same radicular signification. Having reached the medulla oblongata, the vestibular nerve splits into two branches: the ascendant and the descendant. These branches continue on toward different nuclei, principally the nucleus medialis nervi vestibularis (Schwalbe), the nucleus nervi vestibularis spirales (Roller), the nucleus superior nervi vestibularis (Bechterew), the nucleus vestibularis lateralis (Deiters) and the nucleus fastigii, all situated in the region of the IVth Ventricle (Fig. 13). Connections are made with the cerebellum, with the nucleus ruber, with the medulla, and with the nuclei occulomotorii, as well (Fig. 12). Lastly,

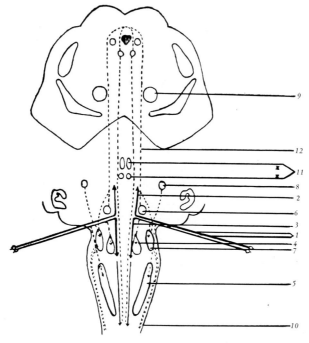

FIG. 13. The central vestibular passages (according to Montandon).

1. First neuron (n. VIII vestibul.).
2. Via ascend. (centripetal).
3. Via descend. (centrifugal).
4. Nucleus triangularis nervi vestibularis.
5. Nucleus nervi vestibularis spinales (Roller).
6. Nucleus superior nervi vestibularis (Bechterew).
7. Nucleus vestibularis lateralis (Deiters).
8. Cerebellous connexions (nucl. tegmenti).
9. Nucleus ruber.
10. Medulla spinalis.
11. Nuclei originis dors. nervorum III et IV.
12. Tractus longitudinalis cornu posterioris.

certain passages, which mostly use the longitudinal posterior fasciculus, reach principally the cortex. The complexity of this structure leads to three important observations:

1.) The principal *vestibular centers* are in the *bulbopro-tuberantial zone;*

2.) *Multiples connections* are made between these centers and other afferent systems of the *equilibrium apparatus,* such as those of *profound sensibility.* This confirms that the vestibular apparatus is the seat of *orientation,* sense of which the active coordinates are diverse.

3.) The *vestibulo-occular* and the *vestibulo-spinal* relations are particularly evident and constitute the support of the *first vestibular reflex arc.*

There exist, lastly, close relationships with the *vegetative* centers which explains the action of vestibular excitations on the vegetative functions, action which is already well established. (Montandon *et Coll.*)

PHYSIOLOGY

ONE OF THE MOST remarkable phenomena of the physiology of the ear is its brief and transitory fatigability, despite the persistance of noise and sounds. This fatigability is not strictly specific for one sound, since it stretches to neighbouring sounds, but it is maximum for the stimulant sound. The duration of the fatigue is directly proportional to the pitch of the sound. Like vestibular fatigability, auditive fatigability is dependent on central factors which hinder objective measurements.

Another significant functional phenomenon is the innervation of the malleus muscles—by the motor nerve fibers of the nervi trigemini—and of the stapes by the facial nerve; in reality the two fibers have their origin in the same cellular column which reaches from the motor nucleus nervi trigemini, in the bulbe, to that of the facial nerve in the prominentia medullae oblongatae. This evidence, whose cybernetic interest is not minor, shows up the function of the two muscles of the cavum tympani. Those have an antagonistic action on the base of the stapes; the musculus stapedius pulls the stapes toward the exterior and tends to make it project out of the foramen ovale (aut fenestra ovalis), along that osseous crista which separates the two foramina, the promontorium. On the contrary, the malleus muscle, by pulling the manubrium of this ossicle inward, works as a tensor on the tympanic membrane and at the same time pulls the platform of the stapes more toward the interior. The simultaneous contraction of the two muscles brings together the ossicles and tightens the tympanum. This contraction is of a reflex order; it is also ultrarapid. It is suppressed by anasthesia. Its role consists of diminishing notably the transmission of deeper sounds and at the same time, by the greater tension of the tympanum, not modifying or favorising that of high-pitched sounds. The depressive action on the lower and more intense sounds protects the internal ear to which they are very damaging. The role of these muscles is completed by that of the Eustachian tube which consists of maintaining the same air pressure on both faces of the tympanum; an optimum condition for its functioning.

To summarize, the vibrations of sound bodies, characterized by their frequency (pitch of sound) and by their amplitude (Intensity of sound) are communicated by the air (or by a molecular medium of a density equally distributed so as to form a medium) and reach the tympanum, through the auditive duct, in the form of pressure variations. The tympanic membrane is thus put into vibration and communicates the form of the wave received to the ossicles which, acting in the fashion of levers, amplify the undulatory intensity while transmitting it to the base of the stapes, the contraction of the muscles of the ossicles diminishing the sensitivity for the deeper tones and acting as a protection.

The movements of the platform of the stapes are transmitted to the endolymph in the form of variations of pressure. These variations, as a result of the inextensibility of the osseous labyrinth ascend the two and one-half turns of the scala vestibuli, return by the scala tympani and finally reach the membrane of the foramen rotundum. The return-depression for the high-pitched tones is found near the foramen rotundum and for the deep tones in the neighbourhood of the helicotrema. In passing from one ramp to another, the vibration crosses the scala media and causes the basilar membrane to vibrate at a point which depends on the pitch of the sound. This constitutes the base of tonal audition. The vibration of the basilar membrane creates at this level microphonic currents which reproduce the form and the frequency of the original sound. These currents have no known physiological significance.

The impulses from the auditive nerve arise in the cochlea. Up to a frequency of about 900 Hz, they can traverse the same nerve fiber with a 1:1 relation; upon reaching 1,800 Hz, the nervous impulse passes alternately in two fibers (2:1 relation); for 2,700 Hz in three fibers (3:1 relation) and so on up to 3,500-4,000 Hz, for which values the nerve impulses are no longer synchronized with the sound waves.

The tone of the sounds depends on the localization of the vibration at a determined zone on the basilar membrane and on the organon spirale; after this the excitation is transported by the determined fibers of the auditive nerve, disposed in a special fashion in the interior of the nerve.

The intensity is relation to the area of the basilar zone put into vibration and the number of acoustical nerve fibers made active, though it is difficult to express this relation in a simple numerical form. In the same way the effect of masking is explained by the intricateness of the activity in the basilar membrane and the rivalry of two tones for the same nervous fibers. The transfer of nerve impulse through the acoustical passages of the cortex, where it becomes conscious, constitutes, finally, the *auditive sensation*.

Differently from the acoustical receptors, the vestibular receptors of the internal ear receive the impulsion coming from the outside directly. Thus there is no transmission apparatus. These impulsions are of two sorts:

1. *Displacements of the head* in one of the three spacial planes (rotational movements).

2. *Changes of the position of the head* (non-rotational, postural modifications). The first are of a kinetic order and influence the cupulae of the semi-circular canals. The second are of a static order and set the otoliths into action.

3. A third mode of stimulation should be mentioned also whose action is manifest at the same time on both the cupulae and the otoliths: that of rectalinear displacement along a horizontal (translation movements) or vertical (elevator movements) axis.

Although the vestibular apparatus is closely integrated in the equilibration mechanism, its specific function, as a sensorial organ, is that of representing the *sense of orientation;* absurd as it may seem, equilibration is a *consequence* of a precise orientative ordinance: in fact, it is through the abandon of the tricoordonometric plan, with which the structure of the posterior labyrinth makes known to us the points of equilibrium possible around our axis of sustentation, that we "lose our equilibrium" in the physical sense of the term; but that conscious (through voluntary fall, or clumsiness) or unconscious (through diverse vestibular lesions) abandon is only possible if the physical limits of the change of orienta-

tion of that axis are passed. It is interesting to note in this connection that these limits can be enlarged considerably by adequate
exercise, just as one can refine one's sense of touch, or one's sense
of hearing or smell; moreover, one should not give "sense of orientation" its popular signification which sees in this concept an
aptitude for directing oneself through a fog, although this notion
includes, implicitly and less clearly, that which we have defined.
It is well known that the mechanism of equilibration also calls
upon, particularly in man, all sorts of other afferences: vision,
profound sensitivity (particularly that of the neck muscles); the
maintenance or re-establishment of spatial equilibrium are not
necessarily related to the functioning of the vestibulum. Nevertheless, the repercussions of disorders of the entire nervous system
on the vestibular functions form an important indication of it in
otoneurological clinics.

The mechanism of excitation of the semicircular canals was
disclosed by a French physiologist, Flourens. A forced rotational
movement of the body in the horizontal or one of the vertical
planes engenders *reactional movements* in the members, the eyes
and the head in the same spatial plane; these movements are
dependent on the corresponding semicircular canal.

Another great physiologist, Ewald, specified that for each rotation of the head there is a corresponding displacement in the
opposite direction of the endolymph contained in one of the semicircular canals. According to whether the current goes in an arc
from the canal to the ampulla (ampullopetal current) or comes
from the ampulla toward the canal (ampullofugal current), the
reactional movements will be in opposite directions. Thus an
ampullopetal endolymphatic current in the right horizontal canal
will create a slow segmentary deviation toward the left and vice-
versa. As to the reactional movement of the eyes or *nystagmus*,
it involves a slow component which obeys the general law; nevertheless, this slow component is only, in the normal human, the
compensation phase of the *rapid active component* which defines
the direction of the *vestibulary nystagmus*. The nystagmus is thus
always in an opposite direction to that of all the other reactional
movements.

We have discussed above the structure and the mechanism of cupular action. Today it is clearly established that the cupula, occupying, in repose, a position determined by its apical and distal attachment points and having thus the conditions of an orthomorphic, stable structure of which the general equation is of the Routh-Hurwitz type, passes, if a rotational movement of the head occurs, into a state of instable metamorphic structure conditioned by the direction of the endolymphatic current. In other words, one has the choice of a cupular deformation of either ampullopetal or ampullofugal; the movement or "inclination" of the cupula can only arise in the case of a traumatic lesion, temporary or permanent, of that organ. These properties permit, now, the exact measurement of the *excitability threshold*, normal or pathological, of the horizontal semicircular canals. This threshold corresponds to the smallest cupular deformation susceptible to produce a regular nystagmic reaction during all of a period of rigorously constant angular acceleration of a determined intensity. (Montandon and coll.)

Besides the segmentary deviations and those of the nystagmus, which constitute the *primary vestibular reflex arc*, the excitation of the vestibulary apparatus engenders a rotational sensation, the *labyrinthine vertigo,* and a vegetative reflex of the depressor type which leads to a nauseous state of which seasickness, due to a violent stimulation of the otholitic receptors, offers a perfect example.

Since the two labyrinths function in a coupled system, it is impossible to interrogate them separately without recourse to artificial means. This is the reason for which we sometimes have recourse to hot or cold irrigation of each of the auditive conduits, with the purpose of provoking analogous reactions to those obtained with the aid of a correct stimulation. We also have recourse to galvanic tests which involve the same inconvenience of inadequation. Lastly, there is direct mechanical stimulation, by *compression* of a labyrinthine fistula, which reproduces in short the fundamental experiment of Ewald on the semicircular canal of a pigeon; it is only rarely possible to realize and has only a qualitative value.

HISTORY

THE UNFLAGGING CURIOSITY which has inspired research relative to the ear from earliest antiquity is only partially satisfied in our days and leaves the field open for numerous complementary observations: the vestibular apparatus, in particular—less favorized than its cochlear neighbour—is not yet the subject of a definitive functional description; the reader will thus not be surprised if the material of this chapter seems to favorize Hearing rather than Orientation: accustomed to thinking of himself as a microcosm, it was natural that man showed a greater interest in the organ which permitted him to hear *and as a result* to orient himself, *this consequence seeming natural to him.* The progress of physiological psychology and that of relative mechanics oblige us to revise such a historical prejudice without however renouncing to describe its evolution.

From the Vth Century before the Christian era, Greek philosophers knew that sound is the propagation of a movement of the air; knowing, from the time of Pythagorus, the laws which relate musical sounds to the length of vibrating cords, they referred the differences of pitch of sounds to the differences of speed of the impulsions given to the air by vibration of cords. Empedocles and his contemporaries also knew the tympanum, the tympanic cavity and the air it contains, to which they accorded a great importance: they thought that the external air in movement could not have an action on the soul unless it met in the body with a substance of the same nature, the *internal air;* they believed this air particularly pure and implanted in the ear during uterine life; such is the *"theory of implanted air"* to which the authority of Aristotle gave the force to live until the XVIIIth Century. Galien was the first to describe the cranial nerves and was familiar with the auditive nerve; he compared the whole of the cavities of the temporal bone to a labyrinth. The poverty of technical means of investigation which were at hand for the ancients suffices to explain the inaccessibility in which the internal and medial ear were situated for them, and at the same time ranges their explanations of hearing in the ranks of speculations.

The Middle Ages brought nothing to the knowledge of the ear that was not already established under Galien. The anatomy of the ear followed the renaissance of that of all the human body under the impulsion of Vesale and the great Italian anatomists of the XVIth Century.

Andrew Vesale (1514-1564) occupied the Chair of Anatomy of the University of Padua at the age of twenty-two. He was also the first to show the organs of which he spoke on a cadaver; the treatise which followed, "De Humani Corporis Fabrica" (1543), revealed an entirely new conception, for it contained numerous drawings according to dissections performed by the author; there are precise descriptions of the temporal bone, the malleus and the incus. The auditive nerve is still considered as a branch of the facial. Vesale's method made for rapid progress in anatomy, that of the ear in particular. His student Ingrassias (1510-1580) discovered the stapes in 1546 and gave a better description of the cochlea and the semicircular canals. Fallopius (1523-1562) studied the development of the ear during the growth progress; his description of the articulation of the chain of ossicles is quite precise, but his credit resides in the discovery of the canal of the facial nerve, still called the Fallopian aqueduct.

Bartholomew Eustachium (1510-1574) published the first work treating the ear exclusively: "Epistola De Auditus Organis" in 1563. His descriptions surpassed those of Fallopius in precision: he describes the tensor muscle of the tympanum and studies it with care—without, however, understanding its role—the morphology of the conduit which was known from antiquity and which remains the Eustachian tube.

The sum of all knowledge thus acquired is found in *De Auditus Instrumento* by Coiter, which appeared in 1572 at Groningue; if this monograph brought nothing new to anatomy, it had the merit of being the first attempt at an interpretation of the functioning of the organ; the author attributed to the tympanum the role of protecting the implanted air, and as to the cochlea, which he believed to be equally full of air, he saw it as reinforcing the sound which acts on the auditive nerve; the Eustachian tube is destined, according to him, to direct the sound from the mouth to the ear, which would permit deaf persons to hear better with their mouths open.

The progress made in Physics open new paths to new hypotheses. After Galileo, Mersenne, a priest, established in 1636 the laws governing vibrating cords, by indicating the relationships of the pitch and the length to the tension and diameter, and noted that a vibrating cord produces harmonics that can be heard when the sound lessens. Guericke shows that air is necessary for the propagation of sound.

Gaspard Bauhin, of Basle, reveals in 1605, a theory of the functioning of the ear based on the resonance of a cavity containing air: when the sound reaches the ear, vibrations are created in its various cavities, below which is found the auditive nerve. The resonance is selective, for these cavities are of different forms and dimensions, the deeper pitched sounds being received in the larger cavities, the higher ones in the smaller cavities. Claude Perrault, doctor, naturalist, physicist and architect of the Colonnade du Louvre takes up the theory of Bauhin in the second volume of his "Essais de Physique" which he devotes to the study of the ear (1680). He reports "implanted air" in the labyrinth and considers the lamina spiralis as the true auditive organ, the stretching of the nerve along this lame having as its effect an increase in sensitivity. It is astonishing to note that none of his predecessors were struck by the fact that the internal air communicated at all times with the external air through the Eustachian tube, as long as it remained in the medial ear! The first modern theory was exposed three years later by Joseph Duverney in his "Treatise on the Organ of Hearing" which is a model of clarity: his three parts correspond respectively to the Anatomy, the Physiology and the Pathology of the Ear. Here one finds a correct description of the transmission of sounds by the tympanum and the ossicles; in the labyrinth which he believed always full of air, he was familiar with the basilar membrane for which he gave the first drawing without attributing to it its role in hearing. He put out, however, a *theory of localized resonance,* almost two centuries before Helmholtz, with the reserve that he situated the reception of deeper pitched sounds at the base of the cochlea, that of high-pitched sounds at the summit. Contrary to Perrault, Duverney thought that the semicircular canals are also parts of the hearing organ, for the reason that since fish and birds have no cochlea and must hear with these canals, he saw no reason for attributing another role to them in man, given an identical composition.

Antonio Valsalva, the celebrated Italian anatomist, dissected more than a thousand ears before publishing his treatise "De Aure Humana" in 1707. He was the first to think that the membranous part of the lamina spiralis was the true organ of hearing. Albert De Haller, in his *Elements of Physiology* (1763), describes the distribution of the branches of the auditive nerve in the vestibulum and the cochlea of the internal ear in which he still saw the "implanted air." He added that the property of distinguishing sounds rests on the speed of the quivering of the acoustical nerve, thus anticipating the telephonic theory of Rutherford.

Lastly, Domenico Cotugno showed in 1760 that the labyrinth is entirely filled with liquid and contains no trace of implanted air, thus destroying a myth which reigned sovereignly for more than 20 centuries. He described the long fibers at the apex of the cochlea and the short ones at the base and correctly localized the deep and high-pitched sounds.

Scarpa crowned the anatomic edifice in discovering the membranous labyrinth and the two fluids of the internal ear, endo- and perilymph. However, the resonantial hypothesis was to know its detractors and its critics. Cramer, in 1741, thought that the fibers of the lamina spiralis were too short to vibrate. Esteve, ten years later, objected that the stretched cords vibrating not only in their totality but also by fractions, a harmonic confusion ought to arise; besides (and this will be picked up a century later against Hemlholtz), the cords are not sufficiently independent to vibrate in isolation.

In Hemlholtz's days, progress in Acoustics had made the problem raised by the perception of sounds appear in all its complexity, while bringing with it elements which would permit of the undertaking to explain this perception. Taking up the experiments made by Mersenne, Sauveur showed in 1701 that the production of harmonics was due to partial vibrations of the cord, accompanied by the principal vibration; thus one could hear such and such harmonic by touching the cord at a point situated at a determined fraction of its length. In 1822, Fourier established, in his "Analytic Theory of Heat," that any function can be considered, and in a single manner, as the sum of a series of sinusoidal functions, differing through their amplitude and their phase relations, and of which the frequencies are all multiples of the same fundamental frequency; the serie is convergent and the function can be represented with an approximation as great as desired on the condition that one has recourse to a sufficient number of terms. The analysis of any periodic function in series by Fourier is applicable to sound vibrations and reunites with Sauveur's experiment: the vibration of a cord is a periodic function analysable in its harmonics, either mathematically or physically. Ohm, known especially for the law of electricity which carries his name, gave in 1843, a psychophysiological prolongation of this theory, affirming that a non-sinusoidal sound vibration gives us the sensation of a complex sound, because we perceive in it the sinusoidal components, the same as those one would find by analysis of Fourier's vibration in series. If certain of the components are not effectively heard in isolation, it is because of their weak amplitude; nevertheless, the aptitude to hear the sinusoidal components of a vibration can be developed through training. In one sinusoidal vibration, we never perceive components: one such vibration constitutes a pure sound. Thus the decomposition of sound vibrations into sinusoidal vibrations which is mathematically and physically possible, *is also a psychological fact.*

Moreover, from 1851 to 1860, the morphology of the internal ear was, thanks to Huscke, Corti, Kolliker, Reissner, Schultze and Deiters practically described. The *theory of the specific energy of the nerves* that Muller had revealed in 1838 ("the same nerve stimulated in diverse manners always gives sensations of the same nature; the same stimulation acting on different nerves produces different sensations") also contributed to the establishment of the works of Helmholtz.

Helmholtz published in 1863 a work, then revolutionary, that he entitled: *Physiological Theory of Music Based on the Study of*

Auditive Sensations. The author recognized therein that the analysis in series by Fourier of a sound vibration is not a purely theoretical operation: he became assured of this by means of resonators, hollow spheres in crystal tubes—which reinforced in the complex vibration the harmonic component to which they had been tuned; this expedient permitted the realization of the physical analysis of a sound and the reinforcement of the harmonic presence too weak to be heard. Helmholtz completed, with his experiments on the synthesis of sounds, the information brought out by Ohm on the analytic power of hearing. By means of tuning forks held by intermittent electromagnets and vibrating in front of the resonators, he produced diverse simple sounds of which the frequencies were multiples of the same fundamental frequency; he could thus rapidly form diverse combinations of the fundamental sound with harmonics of a controllable intensity, reproducing thus, quite a few different sung vowels as well as the sounds of several musical instruments. This apparatus permits one to modify the phases of the partial sounds emitted by the resonators and demonstrated, from this fact, that, contrary to what was believed up to this time, *the musical timbre of a sound depends on the number and the intensity of its harmonic components* and not on their phase relation, nor, consequently, on the form of the vibration. Everything happens as if the ear, instead of receiving the complex vibration as such, was impressed separately by each one of the harmonics; the vibration is thus analysed even if the components are too feeble to be heard and each timbre results from a determined combination of these distinct stimulations. This curious property of the auditive function had, for Helmholtz, as a physical analogy, only the phenomenon of vibration by influence or *resonance;* the whole of his *Theory of Resonance* which derives from this analogy, can be seen in resume in the following significant passage:

"... Suppose the felt pads of a piano have been removed and we sound energetically any note on its harmonic table; we will cause a vibration by influence in a series of cords and more precisely all those and those only which correspond to the simple tones contained in the given note; what happens here, in a purely mechanical manner, is a decomposition of air waves analogous to that which occurs in the ear. If we could attach to each cord of the piano a nerve fiber in such a manner that the latter would be set in motion each time the cord began to vibrate, what would happen would be precisely what happens in the ear, that is that all sounds having contact with the instrument would wake a series of sensations corresponding exactly to the pendular vibrations into which the movement of external air can be decomposed. We would thus hear each of the harmonics individually as the ear does in reality. In these conditions the sensations of the different partial sounds would correspond with different nerve fibers and, consequently, would occur in total isolation."

To complete the theory, Helmholtz assumes too that each resonator corresponds with a determined nerve fiber and that each nerve fiber, when it is stimulated, produces a sensation of definite pitch; each of the fibers of the auditive nerve is thus, according to him, tied specifically to a certain sensation of pitch. Helmholtz thus adopts, giving it a much greater extension, Muller's theory of specific energies; the latter however supposing only five whereas Helmholtz is led, for just the sense of hearing, to suppose as many as there are resonators, which represents several thousand specific energies.

Although the discoveries of Flourens on the semicircular canals were already forty years old, Helmholtz still included the vestibular receptors in the auditive apparatus; he thought that the maculae and the "acoustical" cristae served in the perception of *noises*.

Subsequent works of certain micrographers, such as Hensen and later Hasse led Helmholtz to revise, in the third edition of his work (1870), certain aspects of his theory. He specified that the fibers of the basilar membrane, rather than the pillars of Corti, were the true resonators of the ear; each sound causes vibration by influence of the portion of the membrane where the radial fibers' own sound was nearer to the exciting sound; moreover, here and there in that vibrating region, the vibrations communicate themselves to neighbouring parts of the membrane with a rapidly decreasing amplitude. The vibrations of the basilar membrane transmit themselves to the pillars of Corti and, through them, to the nerve fibers. In summary, according to Helmholtz, the analysis of sounds takes place in the ear and the auditive nerve transmits to the brain a message already analysed in which the diverse pitches are transmitted by distinct fibers; the reception of diverse frequencies is made at determined points in the cochlea owing to the fibers of the basilar membrane which vibrate by resonance under the influence of sounds to which they are attuned.

If the fibers of the basilar membrane can be considered as cords, their frequency is determined by three factors: *length, tension and mass.* Helmholtz dealt only with the first of these and used Hensen's measurements; subsequent measurements showed that the variation of length of the fibers can only take into account the reception of two to three octaves whereas we hear at least ten.

Gray, in 1900, brought in the factor of *tension* for the first time, by showing that the thickness of the spiral ligament decreases from the base of the cochlea to the summit. If one supposes that it tenses the fibers of the basilar, its varying thickness leads to a variation of tension which acts on the fibers' own frequency in the same direction as their variation in length. Lastly, the basilar membrane supports the organ of Corti of which the cells are bigger at the apex; each segment of the membrane is associated with a double column of liquid and the mass thus set into movement by the vibrations grows in the same direction as that of the organ of Corti, which is accorded with the variation of length and tension to permit the conception of differentiation of the resonators along the cochlea. But these resonators, being included in the basilar membrane, are not independent one of the other. One could ask, then, how the perception of a single pitch was possible, when a sound of determined frequency set into motion a certain number of neighboring resonators, which should have as a consequence our hearing several pitches simultaneously. Gray responded to that objection by developing his *"Principle of maximum stimulation"*. The only nerve fiber which provokes a sensation is that of which the stimulation is maximum, that is, that nerve fiber which corresponds to the maximum amplitude in the vibration of the basilar, the effects of the other fibers being suppressed or integrated in the effect of that one. The last hope

of the Resonance Theory was to dim under the weight of the
work in experimental nerve physiology which developed: the "all
or nothing" law formulated by Gotch in 1902, then the research
of Adrian in 1913-14 were opposed to the principle of maximum
stimulation. Otophysiology, passing from mere speculation to
experimental verification, had registered that the greatness of
the nervous influx did not depend on the intensity of the stimulus
once that stimulus attained a supraliminary value.

The three hypotheses of Helmholtz's theory (peripheral analysis of sounds, localized reception of frequencies in the ear, resonance of elements attuned to diverse frequencies) gave rise to
passionate discussions from which new hypotheses grew, founded
on the cerebral analysis of sounds (telephonic theories), on the
peripheral analysis with nonresonantial localization or else on peripheral analysis with cochlear localization of frequencies. It is
interesting to point out that these diverse theories, which have
today only a historical interest, had at the time defenders who
were quite renowned: Rutherford (1886) was champion of the
telephonic theory, Hurst (1894) accepted the peripheral analysis
and the localization without resonance, aided by a mechanical
explanation which is not without relation to the subsequent works
of Von Bekesy; Ewald, developing the idea of the "sound image"
granted the peripheral analysis with localization of frequency
with recourse to stationary waves and to the proportion of inactive
and stimulated fibers that resulted. As to Bonnier, author of a far-
fetched explanation, he excused himself thus: ". . . Thus it is not
by experiment that we will find revealed to us the intimate nature
of auditive phenomena; it will be, in our opinion, excluding the
pleasure from the spirit of all scientific research if we insist on
experimental control of everything. . ."(!)

Fortunately for everyone, far from excluding the spirit of scientific research, as Bonnier feared, experimental control has brought
magnificent results to otophysiology, of which the most remarkable were worth, to their author, Georg Von Bekesy, the Nobel
Prize in Physiology and Medicine for 1961.

The study of cochlear mechanics has given birth to the so-
called "hydrodynamic" theories of audition; several of them,
springing up at the end of the last century, merited this name for

they supposed that the displacements of the stapes in the foramen ovale set into motion the labyrinthine liquid which, itself
displacing the basilar, cause the propagation of a wave along this
membrane. The theories differed as to the form of this wave
which depended on the properties attributed to the basilar membrane; these purely speculative conceptions were not based on
sufficient mathematical study of the functioning of the cochlea
nor upon valid experimentation. The experiments of Von Bekesy,
founded on a solid mathematical base, began in 1928 and were
followed up until very recently, bringing out the solution of a
great part of the phenomena which occur in the internal ear as
well as precise data relative to the mechanical properties of the
membranes which intervene in these phenomena. Supported by
the preliminary calculations of Ranke (1931) and invalidating
the dualist conception put forth by Reboul (1938)—who pic-
tured a central analysis of deeper pitched tones and another
peripheral one for the high-pitched tones—the works of Von
Bekesy developed principally around the study of the mode of
vibration of the basilar membrane, a condition which the author
considered the *sine qua non* for the establishment of an accept-
able theory of hearing. Von Bekesy's first observations were
made upon a model of the cochlea, simplified and enlarged to five
times normal size (Fig. 14). He could thus determine diverse
characteristics of the cochlear fluid after having taken care to
achieve conditions quite close to the actual ones; strong vibra-

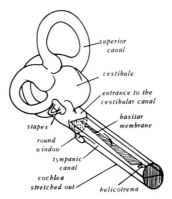

Fig. 14. Model of the cochlea by Von Bekesy.

tions of the artificial stapes, put the liquid into motion and provoked tears in the median membrane (basilar) in several places; the distribution of these zones of action, depending on the elasticity of this membrane, it was possible, in giving it an appropriate thickness, to avoid these accidents and obtain a response at a single point which varied in position with the frequency.

The replacement of the cochlea by a straight tube, as well as various other "anatomic" simplifications, proved themselves as having no consequence on the mode of vibration. Knowledge of the functioning of such a model was extremely precious. When the stapes moves toward the exterior, the membrane raises itself toward the vestibular ramp, at the base of the tube; if the stapes comes back toward the interior, it returns to its resting position or incurves itself in the tympanic ramp. Thus, the wave is created which propagates itself along the basilar membrane in the direction of the helicotrema. If the stapes makes several complete vibrations, the basal part of the membrane follows its movement and vibrates almost in phase with it, the amplitude and the displacements increasing from the stapes up to a certain point, the point of maximum amplitude. Beyond this point a slowing of phase occurs and the waves propagate toward the apex, greatly reduced by the quasi-rigidity of the membrane near the helicotrema. At the point of maximum amplitude of the wave, eddies of which the diameter is equal to the height of the liquid above the membrane, whereas their angular speed is proportional to the amplitude of the movements of the stapes, occur in the two ramps. Modifications of frequency carry the maximum amplitude and eddies toward the stapes for high frequencies, toward the helicotrema for the low frequencies; a satisfactory correlation has been noted between the position of the eddies in the model and the localization of frequencies accepted by the ear. The form of the vibration of the basilar and the position of the eddies are not modified by a change of elasticity of the secondary artificial tympanum, which Von Bekesy judges very important in understanding the fact that diseases of the medial ear do not modify the discrimination of frequencies. In fact, the form of vibration of the basilar membrane seems to depend only upon the basilar membrane's elasticity.

These observations were completed by others on human cochleas carefully prepared according to a technic of micromanipulation entirely conducted in saline solution. The microscopic observation permitted the establishment of the fact that all the structures of the partition which separates the two ramps move together, their displacements being greater at the external edge: in this connection, the cochlear septum (Reissner membrane, basilar membrane, organ of Corti, tectorial membrane) can be considered as a unit. Moreover, direct observation of vibrations permitted the establishment of the existence of a definite distribution of frequencies in the cochlea, distribution concording with those established by other procedures. *The localization of frequencies is thus a definitely acquired fact.* Lastly, owing to the *phase-measuring stroboscope,* Von Bekesy showed that this localization did not correspond to a phenomenon of resonance, but to the propagation, along the cochlea from the stapes to the helicotrema, of trains of waves of which the wave lengths are shorter as the frequency is higher. All these measurements are easily reproducible, with feeble variations from one ear to the other.

The delicate domain of the discrimination of frequencies was also taken up and resolved by Von Bekesy, who showed that the mechanical selectivity of the cochlea does not permit that it alone could have the power of analysis of hearing of lower frequencies. The elastic properties of the basilar membrane, which are very peculiar to it, are responsible at each point for the movements of the cochlear septum and the position of the maximum amplitude; it is thus also to the basilar membrane that, as Helmholtz did and as was generally accepted, the power of discrimination of frequencies by the ear must be attributed.

The work of Von Bekesy has limited the field of possibilities as to theories of hearing. Observations made with the functioning of models correspond with those made on the cochlea itself on the notion of the localization of frequencies since the maximum vibratory amplitude of the cochlear septum moves as a function of the frequency in the classically accepted sense. These same observations definitely condemn the hypothesis of parallel resonators aligned along the basilar membrane and attuned to diverse audible frequencies.

During the past few years, several acousticians have attempted to establish a differential equation which takes into account the mode of vibration observed by Von Bekesy and whose solutions would correspond to the results of his measurements. These highly developed mathematical commentaries differ one from the other in the approximations their authors accept in view of the simplification of their calculations; however the general conception of the functioning of the ear is essentially the same; the sound wave reaches the tympanum, the chain of ossicles, the vibration of the stapes in the foramen ovale gives rise to compression waves in the cochlear liquid which, being practically incompressible, allows undular propagation at a great speed (about that of sound in water). Because of this, the waves reach all parts of the cochlea at about the same time; they set into vibration the system which consists of the cochlear septum and the liquid situated at its contact point, but the coupling between the compression waves and the cochlear septum is only produced at the base of the cochlea where the rigidity of the septum is the greatest. The successive segments of the septum vibrate in phase up to a certain point above which the trains of waves continue, undergoing a greater and greater reduction of strength as they progress. Each segment of the septum set in motion by the difference in pressure which exists here and there in the two ramps responds in function of the local characteristics (mass and elasticity), and the forces exerted upon it by its neighbouring segments; if certain authors use the term resonance in respect to this, it is in a sense which is capable of including all the forms of selectivity in frequency and not in the classical sense which was that of Helmholtz.

The electrophysiology of hearing, rendered possible by the progress in technics of electronic amplification, came into being in 1930 with the experimentation of Wever and Bray. These two physiologists placed upon the auditive nerve of an anesthesized cat an electrode which picked up the variations of potential consecutive to the production of sounds before the ear of the animal; these variation, amplified, were conducted to a telephonic receiver reproducing the sounds emitted in front of the ear: it functioned as a microphone. Thinking they had picked up the potentials of action of the auditive nerve, Wever and Bray at first saw in their experiment a confirmation of the telephonic theory; but they soon saw that the effect that they had produced could also be observed by placing the electrode on the cochlea, even after section or degeneration of the auditive nerve. The phenomena of Wever and Bray thus had its origin in the cochlea itself, which earned it the name of *cochlear microphonic effect*. A more precise selection permitted Davis and coll. recently, thanks to a particular electronic setup and new types of electrodes, to confirm the indubitability of the phenomenon by independent recording of the microphonics and the potential of nervous action. The microphonic effect was found in all the animals which were used in the research; it was also in evidence in humans in the course of surgical operations. The variations of potential set into play are of the microvolt order and can reach the millivolt in certain species for very intensive sounds. The amplitude of the cochlear microphonics is not the same at all points of the cochlea: it is greater at the base for the high-pitched sounds; however, the cochlear microphonic potential is completely distinct from the action potentials of the auditive nerve: contrary to the nervous phenomena, the microphonic potential has no threshold and does not obey Gotch's principle.

It has been displayed for sounds of very low amplitude down to the weakest values disclosed by apparatuses; in contrast with the nervous action potential which always consists of a depolarization and does not thus depend on the direction of the stimulus, the microphonic potential is reversible with the direction of the stimulus. (A stimulatory inversion occurs, for example, when instead of an increase, the stimulus produces a diminishing of pressure on the tympanum.) In the same way, a periodical stimulation in which one abruptly inverts the phase immediately produces an identical and faithful inversion of the microphonics, whereas the action potentials disappear during several periods, reappearing afterwards. Lastly, the latence of the microphonic potential, ranges at $1/10,000$ of a second, is much weaker than that of the action potentials of the auditive nerve which is one-thousandth of a second.

The microphonic exists in the whole scale of audible frequencies and even above that; it has been obtained for infra and ultra sounds, particularly in the guinea pig and the cat. On the contrary, the nervous action potential only goes up to barely 1,000 cycles per second and, if the maximum reached by the auditive nerve is superior to this figure, thanks to a very special mechanism, it remains quite inferior to the highest audible frequencies. Also displayed in the vestibular apparatus, notably by Van Eyck, this phenomenon, of which the purely physical nature is no longer contested, constitutes the ideal image of an energy transducer. Its existence, however, postulates the structural integrity of several elements of the internal ear, integrity without which it does not appear. Some of the work now being undertaken by Professor Rauch in Wurzburg would tend to show that the polarized membrane responsible, as a result of its vibration, for the cochlear microphonic, is Reissner's membrane. Another hypothesis, resting on the measurements by Von Bekesy, tend to place the origin of the cochlear microphonic in the ciliated cells of the organ of Corti: it would be produced by the deformation of the hair cells when the basilar membrane vibrates, a phenomenon which has been related to piezo-electric effect. Von Bekesy had indeed noted that the microphonic had a greater amplitude in the endolymph than in the perilymph. The role of the microphonic effect has not yet been clearly defined and pessimists do not hesitate to qualify it as a useless epiphenomenon. Be that as it may, the application of the microphonic effect to the study of audition has been of great help: its objective character makes it a precious means of investigation in a field which, like that of hearing, is essentially confined to sensation—a subjective phenomenon *par excellence*. Audiograms have thus been established for several different species of mammals; moreover, the precise and objective study of the sounds called "subjective" has also been possible, thanks to cochlear microphonics. If the human ear is stimulated by a pure sound of great enough intensity, the subject hears the harmonics of the sound, called subjective harmonics, as well as the stimulant sound. With two pure sounds, he can also hear a differential sound of which the pitch corresponds to the difference of frequencies of the stimulant sounds; he hears, too, numerous other subjective sounds, called combination sounds, and which represent the associations of the differential sounds and the summation of the sounds of the stimulating frequencies and their harmonics. The aptitude to perceive the subjective sounds varies from one individual to another. In the experiments which have become famous, Wever and Bray achieved the harmonic analysis of the microphonic potential of the cat, finding from 16 to 66 subjective harmonics, according to the band of stimulating frequency, and thus proving the extraordinary variety of sounds created by the distorsion of the vibrations in the ear. Lastly, permitting the achievement of one of the last chapters in the history of otophysiology of hearing, the cochlear microphonic effect was also utilized in the determination of the analysing role of the internal ear, opening, in this manner, the way to the explanation of the transmission of the sensorial message in the auditive nerve.

It is known that the localization of frequencies in the cochlea was long investigated to substantiate Helmholtz's theory; lesions provoked by various means to this end furnished results compatible with the hypothesis of localization without, however, confirming it in detail. The use of the cochlear microphonic rapidly resolved this question. Precise research by Culler has shown that the size of the microphonic varies systematically with the frequency and the position of the electrode: one can thus assign to each point examined an optimum frequency and draw up a cochleogram of the frequencies conforming to the hypothesis by Helmholtz. The very recent work by Davis, Legouix and Tasaki permitted even further restriction of the study of the localization of frequencies: placing special electrodes simultaneously on various contours of the cochlea, they could note that the basal contour gives a response for all frequencies and that this response stretches more toward the apex the lower the frequency. Thus, only the deeper sounds reach the apex, and sounds differing in frequency are differentiated by the greater or lesser extension starting from the base of their response zone; the existence of differences of amplitude in the cochlea and, therefore, its analysing role, can today be considered as established; but the analysis is not accomplished by a series of parallel resonators attuned to diverse frequencies: in this way, if one of the hypotheses made by Helmholtz is def-

initely condemned by experimental fact, the second remains by
the establishment of those same facts.

The last problem to be resolved, that of the sensorial message
in the auditive nerve, was first undertaken experimentally in 1935
by Debyshire and Davis. These authors succeeded in picking up
the action potentials of the auditive nerve by practically eliminating all the microphonics of the recordings with the help of coaxial
electrodes. It is known that the auditive nerve in man has about
30,000 fibers of which the action potentials constitute the sensorial
message. This message expresses, in code, the various characters
of the auditive sensation: the fundamental problem posed to auditive neurophysiology being then to determine how the repartition
of action potentials, in space and in time, between the various
fibers, defines the character of our cortical auditive sensations.

The work of Debyshire and Davis permitted the proving of the
fact that when the ear is stimulated by a pure sound, the action
potentials follow each other along the auditive nerve at a frequency which, for deeper sounds and those of middle pitch, is
the same as that of the stimulant sound; the synchronization is
limited toward the higher pitched sounds to about 3,000 cycles
per second. For the sounds of higher pitch, the response of the
nerve does not reproduce the frequency of the sound received
by the ear. Even so, this synchronization of the action potentials
of the nerve with a stimulatory frequency of the range of 3,000
cycles per second is already a remarkable fact: we know that
nerve fibers have a refractory period which prevents two potentials from following each other at an interval less than 1,000
cycles per second. As concerns the auditive nerve, it has been
shown that, up to about 1,000 Hz, all the fibers respond simultaneously; above that value, the action potential of the nerve diminishes abruptly by half, which indicates that only half of the
fibers function at the same time, or if you like, each fiber only
responds to one period in two of the stimulus; the same phenomenon is produced at about 2,000 cycles per second where each
fiber responds only once in three times: the fibers of the auditive
nerve thus relay each other to reproduce sound frequency up to
3,000 cycles per second. Research by Galambos and Davis, undertaken in 1943, permit the study of the functioning of the first

acoustical neurons and shows that these, endowed with a weak resting activity, each possess a determined frequential threshold: thus, with the increasing of the stimulatory intensity, the same neuron responds to a larger and larger band of frequency. One should note that this band stretches more toward the low-pitched neurons and that it is notably larger for the low-pitched neurons than for the high-pitched neurons. However, even with high intensities, one finds each neuron attuned to a determined frequency for which it furnishes a greater number of action potentials per second than for other frequencies. The transformation of the frequency into spatial coordinates in the cochlea is thus maintained in the auditive nerve and the cochlear nucleus, it is also maintained in the brain, as has been demonstrated by the work undertaken by Tunturi.

The neurophysiological edifice has been crowned by the remarkable "resonance-volley" theory by Wever who attempts to explain the representation of the pitch and intensity in the messages of the auditive nerve: according to this author, the pitch of sounds is given us by the localization for high-pitched sounds, by the frequency of the action potential for the low-pitched sounds and by both simultaneously for the middle frequencies. As to the intensity, its representation is bound by the number of active neurons excited by growing number of fibers which discharge their influx in a single burst or "volley." In a word, the intensity is thus expressed by the number of elementary action potentials per time unit, this number depending itself on the number of active fibers and the frequency of each one of them.

The vestibulary apparatus separated itself historically from its neighbour only in 1823; until then, in fact, all those who were preoccupied with the functioning of the ear had attributed an acoustical function to the posterior labyrinth. It was still granted in Helmholtz's time that its maculae and "acoustical" cristae played a preponderant role in the discrimination of noises. It was in 1823, however, that the French physiologist Flourens published his *Physical Researches on the Properties and Functions of the Nervous System of the Vertebrate Animals,* a work in which his experiments on the semicircular canals of the pigeon and on their determining role in what he called then *"equilibration"* are described for the first time. The genius of Flourens' intuitions did not meet with the success he had the right to expect during his lifetime, and, through a singular concurrence of circumstance, he did not open the way to vestibular otophysiology in the way which would have been logical and desirable. A serious obstruction, at the head of which famous men were found at times, was established and the destiny of Flourens' work was an unjust one that persists even today. For three-quarters of a century he was forgotten. It was then that, toward 1911, the extraordinary work of the otologist De Cyon appeared in Paris, work specifying the work of his predecessor, consecrated the major part of his treatise on the ear to the sense of orientation indissolubly attached to the vestibular apparatus. The end of the last century also brought the results given by Ewald on the assymetry of the endolymphatic vestibular currents, and several decades later, the first histological works of Witmaack on the intimate structural elements of the posterior labyrinth. These works were followed with such assiduity and scientific rigor by Werner of Berlin that they would merit attention for that reason alone. He consecrated to the labyrinth a treatise which has remained a classical. The delicate structure and the ultrastructure of the vestibulum could recently develop due to the use of the electronmicroscope which furnished the histologists with much experimental material from this organ. The most remarkable contributions were made by Bairati, Belanger, Borghesan, Coassolo, R. y Cajal, Ferreri and Crifo, Rauch, Aschan and Wersaell. Most of these authors have not disassociated descriptive histology from functional histology and have thus been led to contribute effectively to the functional physiology of this part of the internal ear. A first attempt in this direction was realized by Steinhausen, Professor of Physiology at the University of Greifswald in 1931. He succeeded in filming *in vivo* in the pike, the modifications of the cupular morphism under the effect of diverse stimulations considered at that time as labyrinthine. As with those of Flourens, the works of Steinhausen knew an impressive number of commentators who built their own thoughts upon the authority of the Master without concerning themselves with their connection to the work of Steinhausen apostles they claimed to be. The fact of the late historic independence of the vestibulary apparatus explains the absence of purely scientific works of synthesis and the profusion of notes, more or less original articles, congresses, reunions, even symposiums and scholarly societies have been consecrated to it. This state of things is the symptom, perhaps heartening, of a scientific activity which, overflowing the framework of speculation without conclusions or restrained clinical application, will lead some day to an explanation of the vestibular mechanism as clear as that of the cochlear.

It must be said, however, that if numerous hypotheses on hearing have confronted each other in the course of time, the general line of research in audiology was to discover by which mechanism hearing was conditioned; this is not the case, unfortunately, in vestibulology where the fundamental problem has been for more than a century, to find out how the ocular nystagmus is produced. This collusion of vestibular physiology and nystagmology is one of the essential foundations for the stamping out of research, in another connection enslaved by cosmonautics and traumatology. It was, therefore, encouraging to see, after Dohlman and Steinhausen, the appearance after the end of World War II of a series of works taking up, in the light of discoveries established in the meantime, the ideas developed by "the second father of the labyrinth," Barany, in 1907. Thus it is that, after Ewald and De Cyon, we saw the appearance once more of mechanistic hypotheses on the vestibulary function, hypotheses of which the most brilliant part was represented by the work of the Dutch physicist Groen (1949). In the very delicate field of vestibular electrophysiology, two names have succeeded in imposing themselves by the merit of the work of their owners: Ledoux, working in Liege, and Trinker, himself a student of Steinhausen, at present Professor of Physiology at Erlangen. These authors have consecrated a large part of their works to the study and the determination of the polarization and depolarization of membranes and to their possible role in the transformation of the vestibular stimulus into nervous influx.

But the vestibular apparatus, for reasons mentioned above, is closely related at present to pathology; otologists submit the vestibulum each day to numerous tests and the methodologies introduced to this purpose have made of the whole of these tests a science: *vestibulometry*. The hypothesis, expressed at the end

of the XIXth Century by Mach and Breuer according to which the
sensorial cells and the crista ampullaris are stimulated by liquid
currents which appear when the head moves in the planes of the
semicircular canals, following the currents produced by the endolymphatic inertia, has also been verified by the electrophysiologists (Lowenstein, Sand, Ross, Katsuki, Van Eyck).

On the other hand, Greiner and Thiebaut at Strasbourg, have
continued the researches of Mach, constructing a special apparatus for this purpose.

These latter have, in fact, shown, in studying the VIIIth vestibular nerve, that when gyratory movements of the head take
place, there are, for each semicircular canal, two opposite reactions: the rotation in one direction increases the number of spontaneous discharges, the rotation in the opposite direction diminishes this number. For the physician, the problem to resolve after
that consists of examining the sensorial mechanism of the vestibular apparatus in the light of the physiological data. It was necessary to explore the vestibular sensation qualitatively and quantitatively, knowing that it manifests itself either by the subjective sensation—sensation of rotation—or by the objective sensation which translates itself particularly by the nystagmic reflex.

Covering thermic stimulation, rotatory or galvanic, numerous
methods came to light which brought their authors fame (Arslan,
Aschan and Bergstedt, Henrikson, Hallpike, Groen and Jongkees,
Montandon and Dittrich, De Vries, Jung and Mittermaier, Jatho,
Torok among the most applied) in the same way the study of
nystagmic movements of the eye, first observed then recorded by
an electromechanical system, finally by an electrographic process,
is improving. These different advances have permitted the development of vestibulometry to its present stage which is the knowledge and the proof of a physiological threshold for vestibular reaction, that is to say a threshold corresponding to the minimum
stimulation capable of setting off and regularly maintaining this
reaction.

Compared to the cochlear ear, and in spite of the great sim-
plicity of the structures to be studied, one sees that the acquisi-
tions of vestibular otophysiology are scanty. In spite of the discoveries of the important nerve centers and channels (Lachmann,

Bergmann and Monnier, P. Montandon, Jr.), in spite of the unanimity existing on the rotatory nature of the adequate vestibular stimulus, in spite of the proofs of an objective sensorial threshold, the intimate functioning, and notably the analysis and the transformation of information received of the vestibular receptor, is still a subject for discussion.

It is for the future, let us hope for the near future, to find the solution of problems still unsolved in the field of the labyrinth.

SECTION TWO

BIOPHYSICS OF HEARING
OR OF THE COCHLEAR SYSTEM

INTRODUCTION

"Me, I schall always be a listener!"

(JUVENAL, *Satires*, I,1.)

IT SHOULD BE considered as an experimental truth, in physics, that sound is transmitted in the form of longitudinal waves transversing the medium material between the source and the ear. It is useful, in respect to this, to remember several elementary notions on the propagation of these waves, called *compression* waves.

To study the propagation of a longitudinal wave in a medium characterized by a density ρ and a module of elasticity E, it is convenient to imagine a cylindrical column of section S stretching indefinitely toward the right. If one causes a constant force F to act from the left extremity on sector S, this force will bring on a displacement at constant speed A from the extremity of the column and adjacent regions, provoking a compression of a region of growing length L, of which the limits S' displaces at a speed C; we give this the name *speed of propagation of compression* or else speed of the compression wave.

The definition of the module E allows us to write as follows:

$$F = ES\frac{1}{L}; (2.1.1.), \text{ for a time } t: F = ES\ \frac{A}{C} ; (2.1.2)$$

The impulsion Ft serves to give a quantity of movement to the medium affected by the compression, of which the speed is A and the mass $M = \rho\, SL = \rho\, SCt$. Now, $Ft = MA$, that is to say $ES \cdot A/Ct$, or even $\rho\, SCt \cdot A$, we deduce:

$$C = \sqrt{\frac{E}{\rho}} \quad (2.1.3)$$

This relation permits the expression of the value of the speed of the compression wave in the elastic material medium.

The strength furnished by force F is expressed by: $P = FA$, and distributes itself in all the region affected by the wave. We obtain the following relations:

$$P = FA = ES \cdot A/C \cdot A = E/C \cdot S \cdot A^2 \quad (2.1.4)$$

We can thus conclude, that across the unity of the section, there passes a force:

$$I = \frac{P}{S} = (E/C) A^2 = DA^2 \quad (2.1.5)$$

to which we give the name *wave intensity*. The intensity of a wave is proportional to the square of the amplitude of the speed communicated by the wave to the medium; the coefficient of proportionality $D = E/C = \sqrt{E\rho}$ expresses the *acoustical hardness* of the medium.

It is naturally possible to localize the energy in the medium. In fact, the medium traversed by the wave possesses, by unity of volume, a cinetic energy $U_K = \frac{1}{2}\rho A^2$. Besides, an elastic medium having been subjected to a compression $(1/L)$ possesses an elastic energy $U_E = \frac{1}{2}E(1/L)^2$. This last expression transforms itself, taking in consideration the relations established above, giving:

$$U_E = \frac{1}{2} E (A/C)^2 = \frac{1}{2}\rho A^2. \quad (2.1.6)$$

The total energy of the unity of volume of the medium in movement is thus:

$$U = U_K + U_E = \frac{1}{2}\rho A^2 + \frac{1}{2}\rho A^2 = \rho A^2 \quad (2.1.7)$$

In an interval of time dt, a volume $S.C.dL$ previously at rest, is occupied by the wave. This necessitates, across section S, a contribution of energy:

$$dW = uSC \cdot dL \quad (2.1.8)$$

thus, by unity of section, a force:

$$I = \frac{dW}{SdL} = u\,C = \rho A^2\,C = \sqrt{E\rho} \cdot A^2 = DA^2 \quad (2.1.9)$$

We see that we thus find the preceding result. (see 2.1.5)

These few data will allow us to approach now the notions of acoustical impedance, of transmission and of reflexion.

The force which traverses a section S, is equal, according to what precedes, to

$$P = (S \cdot D)\ A^2 \quad (2.1.10)$$

This expression resembles formally the expression $P = RI^2$ which gives the value of the force in an electrical receptor of impedance Z. This is the reason for which we can designate the quantity $Z = (S.D)$ by the name *acoustical impedance*, characterizing the conduct of the hardness D and of section S. The notion of impedance permits the simple description of the transmission and the reflection of waves in passage from one conduit to another. It is enough, in fact, to express the equality of the forces transmitted in the two conduits on both sides of the section BB' delimiting sector S. We obtain:

$$P_1 - P'_1 = P_2 \rightarrow Z_1\ (A_1^2 - A'^2_1) = Z_2 A_2^2 \quad (2.1.11)$$

We must besides express the equality of the speeds on the two faces of the surface of separation S:

$$A_1 - A'_1 = A_2 \quad (2.1.12)$$

The resolution of this system of equations gives immediately for the amplitude of the transmitted wave:

$$A_2 = \frac{Z_2 \cdot Z_1}{Z_2 + Z_1} A_1 \quad (2.1.13)$$

For the amplitude of the reflected wave:

$$A'_1 = \frac{Z_2 - Z_1}{Z_2 + Z_1} A_1 \quad (2.1.14)$$

We deduce from this, for transmitted power:

$$P_2 = Z_2 A_2^2 = \frac{4 Z_2 Z_1^2}{(Z_2 + Z_1)^2} A_1^2 = \frac{4 Z_2 Z_1}{(Z_2 + Z_1)^2} P_1 \quad (2.1.15)$$

and for reflected power:

$$P'_1 = Z_1 A'^2_1 = \frac{(Z_2 - Z_1)^2}{(Z_2 + Z_1)^2} Z_1 A_1^2 = \frac{(Z_2 - Z_1)^2}{(Z_2 + Z_1)^2} P_1 \quad (2.1.16)$$

These expressions verify very well the equation of continuity: $P_1 = P'_1 + P_2$. We see that all the power passes from one conduit to the other when there is no reflection in the passage from one to the other. This is notably the case when $Z_2 = Z_1$; the phenomenon of *adaptation of impedances* must in consequence be found in all problems of transmission. When one must join two conduits of different impedance, one must, to avoid losses by reflection, join them by means of a *transformer of impedance* across which impedance Z_2 will appear as an impedance Z_1. For longitudinal waves, this transformation may be realized by means of a system of levers, reducing the amplitude of the speed (Fig. 15).

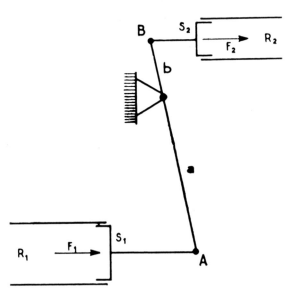

Fig. 15. Transformer (adaptor) of impedance.

We arrive at the desired transformation:

$$P_1 = P_2 \rightarrow Z_1\, a_1^2 = Z_2\, a_2^2 \text{ by making } l_2/l_1 = A_2/A_1 = \sqrt{Z_1/Z_2}$$

When we pass from an elastic medium to a *fluid* medium, the module of elasticity must be replaced by the *module of compressibility*:

$$K = - V\, \frac{\delta p}{\delta v} \quad (2.1.17)$$

For a gas, experience shows that it is the adiabatic compressibility γp which should be used and not the isothermic compressibility p. We know that γ corresponds to the relation of specific heats to constant pressure and to constant volume.

The equations giving the speed of the wave and the hardness of the medium become in this case:

$$C = \sqrt{\frac{P\gamma}{\rho}}, \text{ and } D = \sqrt{P\rho\gamma} \quad (2.1.18 \text{ a}, - \text{b})$$

We can also write, for the speed, in utilizing the equation for the state of gases and the definition of density:

$$C = \sqrt{\frac{\mu RT}{V} \gamma \frac{V}{\mu M}} = \sqrt{\frac{\gamma RT}{M}} \quad (2.1.19)$$

(μ represents the molar mass and M the molecular mass.)
This last expression of the speed brings out the influence of the temperature on the speed of waves.

Having brought to memory some very general results on the propagation of compression waves in various media, it is now necessary to restrict this study to sound waves only, that is to waves susceptible of provoking, by means of the ear, an auditive sensation. A single leap in pressure, as we have envisaged heretofore, is only received by the ear as a discomfort, until the pressure on all parts of the tympanum is equilibrated: it does not produce an actual auditive sensation. The auditive sensation only occurs after repeated variations of pressure in rapid succession, but not necessarily periodic. It is convenient for studying this type of variation, to consider successively periodical simple waves, periodical complex waves, and finally nonperiodical waves.

According to what has gone before, we can divide waves into two classes: those which have periodicity and those which do not. This classification corresponds approximately to the subjective repartition of phenomena into *sounds* and *noises*, that is into pleasant sonic manifestations and unpleasant ones.

The periodic movement which is simplest is that of a mass attached to a spring; it is represented in function of time by a sinusoid: $y = Y \sin 2\pi v E = Y \sin 2\pi E/T$ in this expression Y is the amplitude of the movement, v is the frequency, $T = 1/v$ the period. The sound wave which provokes a sinusoidal movement of particles of the medium it traverses is a sinusoidal wave. Such a wave, running through a cylindrical conduit produces

there a series of compressions and rarefactions, each successive zone repeating the movement of those which precede it
with a growing retardation proportional to the distance. We call
the *wave length* the distance which separates two zones of which
one has a retardation of a period on the other. The wave
length λ and the period T are thus related by the relation: λ = CT
where C is the speed of propagation.

Some Important Numerical Values

	Speed C at 35° Centigrade	*Hardness D*
Air	3.5 . 10^2 m./s.	4 . 10^2 K/m²s.
Water	1.4 . 10^3 m./s.	1.4 . 10^6 K/m²s.

We have said above that the ear experienced an auditive sensation when the wave which hit it provoked variations of pressure
in rapid succession. The study of sinusoidal waves permits the
specifying of this point: the ear experiences an auditive sensation
for waves of a frequency between 20 and 20,000 cycles/second,
or about 10 octaves. The highest frequencies correspond to the
shrillest sounds, the lowest frequencies to the deepest sounds.

These limits vary among individuals; we also observe a progressive loss with age of sensitivity to the highest frequencies. Thus
the limits of hearing can only be approximately fixed, the choice
of a limitation being dictated by practical necessities (audiometry). Above a frequency of 20,000 cycles/second we speak of
ultrasounds; infrasounds below 20 cycles/second.

If the frequency of the wave determines the height of the perceived sound, the intensity of the sensation is determined by the
intensity of the wave, which itself depends on the amplitude.

To obtain quantitative information on the functioning of the
ear, we have recourse to acoumetric and audiometric methods
during which we ask the subject about his own sensations. The
choice of tests susceptible of giving the most objective information is the principal rock of audiometry. The measurements most
employed because they are the most physiological, are the
thresholds. By definition, the threshold of a sensation is the smallest value measurable objectively of the stimulus which provoked

the sensation. We thus determine the *absolute threshold for hearing* by the smallest value of the intensity of the wave which provokes the sensation; the *differential threshold of intensity* by the smallest variation of intensity perceptible; the *differential threshold of frequency* by the smallest variation of frequency perceptible.

The results of the determination of the absolute threshold of intensity are represented in function of the frequency by *curve 1* in Figure 16. *Curve 2* here indicates the intensity at which the

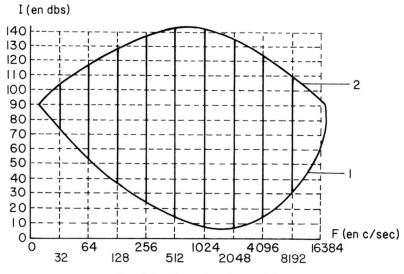

Fig. 16. Normal auditive field.

sensation becomes painful. The field of hearing is shown by the hatchured surface, the frequencies which limit it can be defined as the frequencies above which painful sensation is reached before auditive sensation.

The reader will notice that we have chosen to represent acoustical intensities in Figure 16, a logarithmic scale: it would in fact be impossible to represent on a linear scale a size where the variation extends from 1 to 10^{12}. The choice of unity for this scale is suggested by the results of the measurement of differential thresholds of intensity. We find, in fact, that in large limits, the ear is not sensitive to an increase of intensity inferior to 25 p/c. If, thus, we start with a sound for which the intensity is taken as unity, the tightest scale of intensity, for which the degrees are distinct, forms a geometric scale of ratio *1,25*, which is more or less equal to $\sqrt[10]{10}$. We call the degrees of this scale *decibels* (dB); 10 decibels here correspond to an intensity relation of 10 to 1; in general, an interval of D decibels describes an intensity relation of $10^{D/10}$. An intensity relation R is represented by an interval of $10 \log_{10} R$ decibels.

If we fix the origin at the threshold of hearing for frequency: $v = 1.000$, ($I_0 = 10^{-12}$ Watts/m² or 10^{-16} W/cm²) the scale can be used for absolute measurements. The painful sensation is attained for all frequencies when the intensity is 10^{12} times superior ($= 1$ Watt/m²), that is 120 decibels above the threshold; we write this as 120 decibels, reference 10^{-12} Watts/m².

We have said that the threshold of hearing is not the same for all frequencies: in effect, it meets the pain threshold for the extreme frequencies of the acoustical field. The result is that curves of equal sensation (isosonic) do not coincide with curves of equal stimulus. For example, curve 60 (Fig. 17) corresponds to

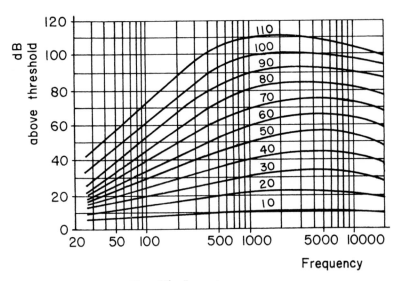

Fɪɢ. 17. Isosonic curves.

sounds subjectively as intense as a sound of 60 decibels at 1,000 cycles/second. We say that all sounds united by this curve are on the isosonic of 60 *phones*. The scale of phones and that of decibels only coincide at the frequency of 1,000 cycles/second. We note that the subjective intensity grows more rapidly for very deep sounds than for very shrill ones. The differential threshold diminishes toward the extremities of the acoustical field. Thus it is that, despite great differences of values of the acoustical threshold, all the sounds, at high levels, appear of the same intensity. The knowledge of isosonic lines is indispensable to problems of construction of amplifiers destined to measure noise or to reproduce sound.

When the oscillation of particles in the medium, while periodic and having a well-defined period, is not sinusoidal, the sound is called *complex*. A complex sound can always be described by a superposition of sinusoidal waves of which the frequencies are whole multiples of the fundamental frequency. (Fourier's theorem.) The search for the amplitude to attribute to each of these waves, called *harmonic waves,* to conveniently represent the complex sound, is called *harmonic analysis.*

The voice, notes obtained by means of musical instruments, are complex sounds. The harmonics which accompany the fundamental frequency give these sounds their characteristic timbre. The fact that the ear is equal to distinguishing the timbres of sounds shows that it possesses a means of achieving harmonic analysis. It can also analyse mixtures of sounds without harmonic relation, as the series of *partials* produced by the vibration of certain objects (bell, etc.), or more simply the *tutti* of a symphonic orchestra, or else the notes played simultaneously by various instruments of the same orchestra.

When the oscillation of the particles of the medium have no precise periodical character, we can describe the sound which is produced as *confused*. A harmonic analysis effected on a confused sound reveals a continuous spectrum of frequencies. If all the audible frequencies are represented, we speak of a "white noise," in analogy with the white light, which contains all the "colours" of the light spectrum.

From the objective point of view, the different waves which constitute the complex sound are independent, the intensity of the whole is thus equal to the sum of the intensities of the components.

From the subjective point of view, it is more difficult to foresee what the perceived intensity will be, because we still do not wholly understand how the brain achieves the integration of partial sensations. The evaluation of the total level of a noise is made in practice by the summation of the subjective intensity, taking into account the isosonic curve corresponding to the total intensity.

The principal particularities of the functioning of the ear being described, it is left for us to see in what measure we can attribute a precise functional role to the different parts of this organ. For this we will follow the sound wave on its journey, from the exterior air until the terminations of the auditive nerve, passing by the conduit of the external ear, the chain of ossicles and the cochlear ramps. The sound, as such, goes no farther; we can only make hypotheses or imagine analogies to attempt to understand how the astonishing analysis of complex sounds is accomplished. In reality, the limit assigned to the exact sciences is attained at the moment when the sound wave, having touched the terminations of the auditive nerve, gives rise to a nervous influx and penetrates the conscious.

COCHLEAR MECHANICS IN SHORT

Rocard consecrates in his *Dynamique Générale des Vibrations* an important chapter to the propagation of plane waves in the pavilions. He describes there the diverse mathematical characteristics leading to the calculation of the amplifying power of the acoustical pavilions. This power can every day be observed at the level of the ear pavilion.

Thus, the role of the external ear, pavilion and auditive conduit is to concentrate as much as possible the sound energy on the tympanic foramen.

The chain of ossicles of the middle ear transmits this energy from the tympanic membrane to the foramen ovale—the entrance to the internal ear. From the mechanical point of view, there is an adaptation of the impedance of two conduits: the external auditive conduit, which contains air (acoustical hardness D_1) and presents a section S_1 (about 60 mm) and the cochlear ramp which contains the endolymph, a liquid which can be assimilated in water as to its mechanical properties (hardness D_2) and which presents a section S_2 (about 4 mm). According to the relations noted above, the transfer of energy will be made without reflection when $A_1^2 S_1 D_1 = A_2^2 S_2 D_2$ or A_1 and A_2 represent the amplitude of the wave in the internal and external ear respectively. With the values indicated on the table as above shown this relation gives:

$$\frac{A_1}{A_2} = \sqrt{S_2 D_2 / S_1 D_1} \cong 15 \quad (2.2.1)$$

The study of the articulation of the ossicles shows that a reduction of this order is in fact obtained between the movement of the part of the malleus which has contact with the tympanic membrane and the platform of the stapes which closes the foramen ovale. The passage of the sound energy is thus assured of air until the endolymph with a minimum of loss.

It is even very difficult to experiment in the middle ear, but until the last few years, work on the interior of the internal ear was avowed practically impossible. This is the reason for which theories which attempted to take into consideration the characteristics of hearing leaned more on hypotheses than on experiments; thus is the celebrated theory by Helmholtz which sees in the some 23,000 radial fibers of the basilar membrane as many resonators, each harmonized to a different frequency.

But for about thirty years progress in experimental technics has permitted acousticians to prodigiously develop their research. The works of Von Bekesy, in particular, have opened a new chapter in the physics and physiology of the ear. In showing how sound energy is propagated in the internal ear, from the foramen ovale to the terminations of the auditive nerve, they have brought back the limits of scientific study of the auditive process.

The study of the properties of hearing led Helmholtz to postulate the existence, in the internal ear, of a series of oscillant systems susceptible to enter into resonance, each on different frequencies. It is these systems which would transmit the vibrations of the endolymph to the auditive nerve. Intensive research, notably on the differentiation of frequencies and on sounds in rapid succession (trills), permit Helmholtz to specify the number and the deadening of the resonators of the ear. The model proposed by Helmholz retains all its value as a description of a simple mechanism which takes into account the principal properties of the ear. But the tentative anatomical identification of the resonant elements has not been as successful. We have had to abandon the appealing idea of assimilating the 23,000 radial fibers of the basilar membrane into the cords of a sort of piano in miniature which would enter into vibration in the manner of a frequency meter, when the sound wave which touches them contain the frequency with which they are attuned. Although a correspondence has been established between the position of lesions of the organ of Corti and the pitch of sounds of which perception was affected—the nerve endings affecting the lowest frequencies being localized at the upper extremity of the cochlea, whereas the high frequencies are received by the shortest fibers situated near the foramen ovale—the experiments made since 1927 by Von Bekesy and his collaborators have shown that the mechanism of excitation of the auditive nerves is, in reality, much more complex. By a series of experiments calling for all the resources of modern technics, Von Bekesy has studied the propagation of the sound wave in the internal ear and the deformations it creates on the membranes which contain the nerve endings. The result of these studies has been that one never observes for any frequency on the basilar membrane the stationary wave which one would expect if it was made up of independent juxtaposed resonators. In reality, for every frequency there is always a corresponding progressive wave which propagates itself along the membrane and produces there characteristic periodical deformations.

By studying in greater detail these deformations (Fig. 18) we

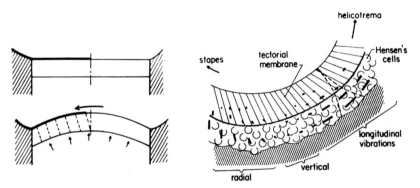

FIG. 18. *Left:* The organ of Corti represented as a device to match the mechanical impedance differences between the perilymph and the stiffer tissues of the organ. The matching is made for shearing forces.
Right: The distribution of the radial and longitudinal vibrations along the organ of Corti for stimulation with a tone, seen through the Reissner's membrane. (According to Von Bekesy.)

note that they change in form in the course of the passage of the wave. Transversal in the plane of the membrane near the foramen ovale they pass in a short transition zone to a transversal perpendicular disposition in the plane of the membrane and then become longitudinal up to the summit of the ramp.

The position of the zone of transition between the two modes of
vibration changes with the frequency: it comes closer to the
foramen ovale as the frequency increases.   One can consider
that the endings of the auditive nerve are not sensitive to all the
deformations of the basilar membrane indifferently, but more
particularly to those which are produced at the level of the
transition zone which replaces, to some extent, in this undulatory theory of the internal ear, the zone occupied in the Helmholtz model by resonators attuned to the corresponding frequency.   A new and interesting aspect of the hydrodynamic
study of the waves which cross the internal ear is the problem
of transfer of sound energy from the endolymph to the rigid

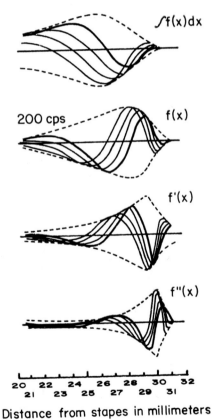

Distance from stapes in millimeters

Fig. 19. See text (according to Von Bekesy).

tissues which contain the auditive nerves. The great sensitivity of the ear gives us an inkling of an excellent adaptation of impedance in the direction of a new diminishing of amplitude.

Figure 18, borrowed from a monograph by Von Bekesy, shows how forces acting by pressure on the basilar membrane can produce important cutting efforts on the interior of a thick elastic membrane partially covered by an inelastic membrane. The anatomical conformation of the organ of Corti responds to this definition. Cuttings are produced between the reticular membrane and the tectorial membrane as well as between the latter and the basilar membrane.

Thus, the analysis of the movement of sound waves in the internal ear has permitted the drawing back of the limit of the field open to quantitative interpretations (Fig. 19). The sound wave is followed from there on from the source to the tissues which contain the receptors of the nervous system. What happens beyond is not in the field of physics and crosses the threshold of biophysics.

PHENOMENOLOGY OF ACOUSTICAL PERCEPTION

I T IS EASY TO SHOW by elementary experiments that there is no absolute measurement of pitch and sound intensity. One can tap a tuning fork giving A_3 at some distance from the auditor and approach it to his ear, and it will seem to him that the sound becomes deeper and deeper: one can even make this fact the more evident in an objective manner by asking the subject to sing at the same pitch as the tuning fork.

Stevens has studied quantitatively the relation between pitch and intensity to this effect, he had one person listen alternatively to two pure sounds of slightly different frequencies and asked him to regulate the intensity of one of the two until he judged both pitches equal, having thus compensated the difference of frequency by a difference of intensity. The results are reported in the diagram of Figure 20, where we see in ordinates the relative difference of frequency and in abscissas the intensity: we note that the growing intensity raises the pitch of shrill notes and lowers that of deep ones considerably. On the other hand, the effect is weak for the middle tones.

Thus, frequent modifications of intensity of very high or very low sounds in a musical work can lead to *perceptible discordances,* though hardly noted in the median range. The variation of pitch and intensity shows up to a lesser degree in the listening to complex sounds (Fig. 20).

It is legitimate to imagine how much the complex sounds can be "out of tune," in particular the sound of certain pipes of the mouth organ which furnish nonharmonic parts. A complex sound should not have too many components, nor reach too great intensities. This poses particularly delicate problems for the constructors of electronic instruments. Some achieve the synthesis of timbres by using exact harmonics furnished by electrical oscilla-

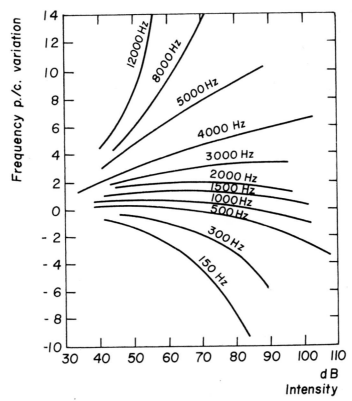

Fig. 20. Variation of the pitch of sounds in function of their intensity.

tors: these harmonics have multiple frequencies of the fundamental, but can seem out of tune for the reason we have just explained.

The temporal loss of intensity of sound given by the piano also produces a disharmony in the direction of high frequencies. It is certain that in this case this disharmony contributes to the constant variation of musical sound that the ear insists on for a good aesthetic impression. It is in the range which extends from 1000 to 2000 Hz that the variation of pitch is the weakest. We could even say with greater tolerance that sounds between 800 and 3000 Hz are of quite stable pitch. In fact, the disharmony which intervenes in the variation of the intensity of the sound can be considered as a pleasant stimulation of the ear only if it remains weak; sounds which have a fundamental superior to 3000 Hz are not well adapted to musical usages, nor are deep and intense sounds which are not always to be recommended for accompaniment.

The laws which we have just established relating the pitch of sounds to their intensity are only valid for notes of rather long duration, of sinusoidal character or where transitory qualities are not too brusk. If we take up analogous research to that which we have already cited, for repeated sound impulsions of short duration (¼ s), we notice that all the notes are displaced downwards by ¼ or ½ a tone, no matter what their pitch. This is the most general case in musical practice, where held notes are only exceptional.

But if we superpose a permanent noise on the short sounds, which are the object of our experiment, the disharmony is only produced in certain cases and not at all for medium frequencies, around 500 Hz (C_4). This case can also occur in musical works when certain instruments give out brief sounds above the rolling of drums, cymbals, etc.

Among the numerous researches that have taken these phenomena as object, we must cite particularly those of Langenbeck, who has given great study to the adaptation of the ear, to which we will return. It is extraordinary that a musician should not be aware of these variations of pitch, for example, when he plays one after the other *forte* or *piano* on a violin; in reality, the effects of intensity on the pitch are frequently attenuated by other phenomena. For instance, the perception of the fundamental of a complex sound does not come only from the hearing of the first harmonic itself, but also the hearing of *differential sounds* which are produced between the superior harmonics and which we will study later on.

Let us lastly note that the sounds which contain nonharmonic art (bells, triangle, etc.), do not possess a definite fundamental since the series of their parts give very varied differential frequencies.

In musical practice, disharmonies which result from variations of pitch of complex sounds are not very perceptible, for we recognize intuitively the following restrictions:

1) In general, the pitch of fundamental used in music is no more than 3500 Hz.
2) The spectrum of a *mezzo forte* sound in the medium range (about 300 Hz) rarely contains more than ten to twelve important parts.
3) We proscribe, as much as possible, sounds in permanent system.

These restrictions allow us to explain why the extension of the technics of electroacoustical reproduction at very high frequencies (up to 15000 Hz) has not shown itself as profitable as one could hope as concerns musical quality.

Nevertheless the evolution of composition for the last two hundred years has constantly tended to increase and vary the dynamic sound, to amplify the orchestral masses, and to extend the register of pitch, which results in a progressive diminishing of the "purity" of the sound object in the vertical as well as the horizontal direction.

Let us now examine what happens when we hear two different notes either simultaneously or one after the other: we note that the intervals, *harmonic* and *melodic*, which separate them have different properties. Anyone can easily demonstrate this phenomenon if he has at his disposition a well-tuned piano. If we sound simultaneously the notes C_3 and E_3, then A_6 and C_7 sharp, we perceive in both cases an identical harmonic interval, the third tempered major. But if we hear the two intervals in the course of a melody (melodic intervals), we notice that the interval $C_3 - E_3$ seems much greater than the interval A_6-C_7 sharp, which is higher by almost four octaves.

The experiment is even more conclusive if we do not take a melody with a tonal character where the harmonic perception has a great importance, but rather arbitrary intervals: we would compare, for example, the melodic suites $B_2-C_3-E_3-G_3$ sharp and G_6 $-A_6-C_7$ sharp $-F_7$. This observation will perhaps seem even more significant if we successively play five neighboring notes in the middle octaves, then the five corresponding notes in the high octaves of the piano, sounds which will seem much closer to each other than the first notes played. What is happening here is the working of a property intrinsic to perception, of the same order as

the estimation of the scale of pitch which presents no character
of proportionality with frequencies or intensities of tone parts.

A study conducted by Feldtkeller and Zwicker with a great
number of subjects has shown that we perceive in general the
same difference of melodic interval between the notes A_6–E_7,
which form a fifth as with the third C_3–E_3. Thanks to such studies,
we can build a scale of appreciations of intervals by having a large
number of listeners recognize an interval which seems the same
melodic size as a given interval but in another scale. Such a scale
is that represented by Stevens and Volkmann in Figure 21; in ab-

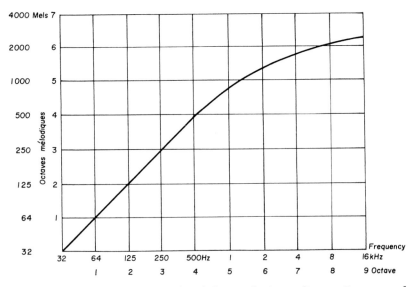

FIG. 21. Scale of appreciation of melodic pitch (according to Stevens and
Volkmann).

scissas the frequencies are shown in logarithmic coordinates,
whereas the melodic intervals are shown as ordinates of which
the unit is *mel*, defined by giving the value of 1000 mels to an
average sound and a frequency of 1000 Hz.

The harmonic and melodic intervals remain confused up to
about C_4 (500 Hz), but the diminishing of melodic intervals becomes perceptible above C_5: this is another reason for not using,
in music, sounds whose fundamental is higher than 3500 Hz (A_6).

The scale of sounds currently used (which corresponds to the range of the piano) covers seven harmonic octaves but only five melodic octaves; an interval of an octave in the very high tones (frequency relation 1/2) only corresponds to a pitch relation equal to 1/10.

The result is that it is difficult to perceive the sequence of notes in a very high range, because the melodic degrees are too small and resemble each other too much. On the other hand, there is no difficulty in extending a polyphony to such heights, for the harmonic appreciation only depends on the relation of frequencies, no matter what the pitch.

No more than acoustical frequencies is the intensity of sound phenomena measured directly by the ear. Its perception is regulated by the physiological law of Weber and Fechner, valid in first approximation for all sense organs, which affirms that the relative increase of sensation is proportional to the logarithm of the exciting quantity, here expressed in decibels (Fig. 22, dotted curve).*

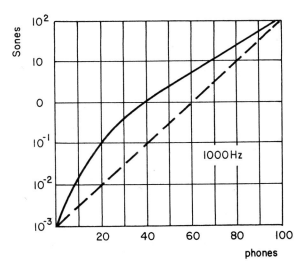

FIG. 22. Subjective scale of sonorities (according to *Elektronische Rundschau*, Berlin, 1955).

*Remember that 10 decibels represent a relation of intensities of 10 to 1, and that we attribute the value O dB to the sound intensity 10^{-16} W/cm², which is quite close to the perception threshold at 1000 Hz.

Since the sensitivity of the ear is not the same for all the frequencies, it is necessary to take it into consideration, like Fletcher and Munson. Taking as reference the logarithmic scale of sensations for sounds of 1000 Hz, they have determined more and more closely to the other frequencies the intensity of sounds which procure the same sensation of sound force (or sonority) as that of sounds of 1000 Hz frequency and of known intensity. At each frequency, the scale obtained is perceptibly logarithmic.

The levels of apparent sensation, that is the levels of sonority, are expressed in *phones*. At all frequencies, the quantity 0 phone represents a sound which is just barely audible. Sounds with 10 phones are those which have the same sonority as a sound at 1000 Hz of intensity 10 dB above the threshold, etc. The scale of phones and that of decibels thus coincide at 1000 Hz, averaging a slight staggering due to the fact that the quantity 0 dB at 1000 Hz (hearing threshold) does not exactly correspond with the acoustical intensity 10^{-16} W/cm taken as reference. Above 120 phones, the sound pressure creates on the ear a painful sensation (*pain threshold*).

If we regulate the level of a radio lower than the original recording in the broadcasting studio, the low frequencies are relatively weaker than the medium, the timbre is altered and the sound object loses its "volume." On the other hand, spoken words too loudly regulated will seem a bit hollow because of the accentuation of the deep tones. Potentiometers of *tonality correction* permit the reduction of this sort of distortion.

Curves of equal sonority furnish no information on the scales of sensation, in particular they do not permit the definition of the relation of two sensations (a sound twice as loud as another, etc.). We have tried to perfect a purely subjective scale of sonorities expressing the "force of sound," of which the unit is called *sone* (Fig. 22). It is defined as being the sonority of a sound of 1000 Hz at 40 dB above the threshold, heard with both ears. An elevation of 30 to 90 sones, for example, signifies that the sound appears to be three times louder.

In music we only use a reduced portion of the scale of sonorities. Besides very weak sounds are, in a room, covered by the surrounding noise, the sound intensity must be greater than this

quite off-key. The held note does not only produce modifications of sonority, but systematic discords that we can compare to a pathological phenomenon, "diplacousie": in this disease, a sound is not perceived with the same pitch by both ears within a limited field of frequencies and the sound can even appear double. Stumpf showed in 1883 that diplacousie appears in a very minor way in a great number of normal individuals, caused by the unequal sensitivity of the two ears.

The auditive fatigue which accompanies a prolonged overcharge of sound explains the role played in music by silences, particularly important after *fortissimi*, after which they leave time for the ear to re-establish its normal sensitivity. Let us note on this question that the sound only disappears progressively during the pause because of the reverberation in the hall, and the musical role of pauses depends partially on this slow decreasing of sound.

The thick lined curve on Figure 24 is relative to another phenomenon provoked by the adaptation of the ear, which is the decreasing of the differential thresholds of perception of intensity and pitch: we perceive better than under normal conditions the modulations of amplitude and pitch of sounds which follow a held note. Maximal sensitivity appears only after a minute, when the diminishing of intensity appear instaneously. Adaptation then signifies greater differentiation.

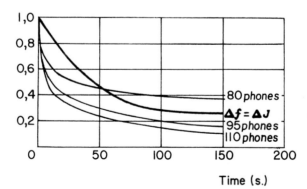

Fig. 24. Adaptation of the ear to sounds of diverse intensities. The fine-lined curves show the dimunition of the sonority. The thick-lined curve expresses the relative diminution of the threshold of perception differential of pitch ($\triangle f$) and intensities ($\triangle J$) during the emission of the held note. (According to Von Bekesy.)

Lastly, prolonged sounds of sufficient intensity mask high notes for more than an octave above them although they do not at all mask lower sounds: long bass accompaniments (at the organ for example), have thus important repercussions on the song of higher range.

In summary, a held note of quite long duration and great intensity strongly influences the simultaneous or following musical sounds, as much by its action on the sound level and the apparent pitch of neighboring notes as by the effect of masking of higher frequencies and the temporal variations of the auditive sensitivity to small differences of pitch or intensity which give the life to sound: briefly, its influence reaches to the totality of the structure of sound objects.

GENERALIZED EXPRESSION OF THE
AUDITIVE SENSITIVITY

In a statistical study with 400 subjects, men and women, equally divided, grouped in seven age classifications (1: = 15 to 19 years, 2: = 20 to 29 years, etc.) Dittrich and Fumeaux have confirmed the classical data of presbyacousie or auricular senescence. Auditive losses in decibels (dB) observed by age and by frequency, calculated statistically, correspond to the values determined by Bunch, Leisti, Sataloff and others.

The table below indicates auditive losses observed in their statistical study on their subjects taking into account the seven age classifications and frequencies. (Fig. 25. The surface of the

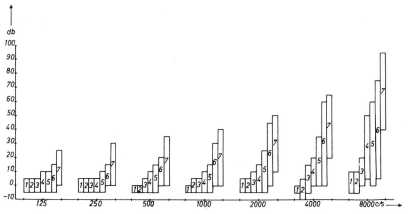

Fig. 25. See text (according to Dittrich and Fumeaux).

rectangles represents the dispersion of the minimum thresholds, the short sides indicating the minimum and maximum values of the dispersion, the number 1 to 7 representing the age classifications.) These authors point out here:

> —that the dispersion is accentuated as the age classifications represent more aged subjects;

79

—that the dispersion is accentuated as the frequencies are higher;

—that the two phenomena combining, the dispersion is important for aged subjects at high frequencies.

Taking into consideration the notion of Hood's *critical sound level,* that is of sound intensity of industrial noises liable to provoke a sound traumatism, a lesion of the peripheral receptor organ (organ of Corti), eighty subjects, separated into groups of twenty and combining the age classifications four, five, six and seven were examined.

These subjects had been employed in an activity in a sound environment nearing the critical sound level during one or several decennaries. The sound intensity of the work environment is well known since the work done by Hood then by Mounier-Kuhn, permitting the selection of these 80 subjects.

The statistical study of auditive losses has shown that by frequency and by age classification, *hypoacousis,* the loss in decibels, was considerably more pronounced than in senescence. No audiometric tracing showed a curve of the type "professional deafness."

We then felt it necessary to ask ourselves if it was a question of a diminishing of the auditive acuity, of a premature aging of the peripheral receptor organ of subjects who have worked in a sound environment which was infracritical, since the audiometric curves obtained were superposable in their form to that of a presbyacousis.

The audiometric facts have led us to make a mathematical analysis of the audiometric curves in order to confirm the existence of that which is called: *professional chronic sound traumatism* as to professional deafness and presbyacousis.

Thus a simple statistical study of presbyacousis confirms, with a few corrections, the observations made by authors who have already treated this subject.

The conditions of a statistical analysis could not be united because of the fixity of the bidistributional coordinates, so it seemed to us more interesting to submit the obtained results to a *sequential analysis* of their representative graphic functions. This is, in fact, the only means to which one can revert to obtain new elements as well as to verify the value of the relations that the clinical experiment has introduced.

The graphic representation of a function, possibly characteristic of the auditive sensitivity, involves, first of all, the choice of a positive scale of values. We have chosen to represent in abscissas, in *logarithmic scale*, the frequencies: $0 = 128$ c/s, $1 = 256$ c/s, $2 = 512$ c/s, $3 = 1.024$ c/s, $4 = 2.048$ c/s, $5 = 4.096$ c/s, $6 = 8.192$ c/s or

$$x = \log_2 \frac{v}{128} \quad (v = \text{frequency})$$

and in ordinates, in *linear scale*, the intensities progressively growing to 0-56 dB. (In reality the two scales are logarithmic, the decibelometric scale representing a logarithmic function by definition. The scale of intensities had nevertheless to submit to a translation of the mean values observed through the existence of a zero graduation on the audiometers. This translation is without effect on the form of the functions represented.)

We can thus see on Figure 26 the comparative diagrams obtained for normal auditive sensitivity, presbyacousis and in the case of chronic professional sound traumatism. Each curve corresponds to the age classifications previously determined, or:

		15-20 years	(XI)	class I
a)	normal sensitivity	20-29 years	(X)	class II
	(in dotted lines)	30-39 years	(IX)	class III
		40-49 years	(VIII)	class IV
		50-59 years	(VII)	class V
b)	presbyacousic sensitivity	60-69 years	(VI)	class VI
	(in cruciform lines)	70- years	(V)	class VII
		40-49 years	(IV)	class IV
c)	sensitivity in case of c.p.s.t.	50-59 years	(III)	class V
	(in continuous lines)	60-69 years	(II)	class VI
		70 years	(I)	class VII

The analysis of this graph confirms, first of all, the conclusions by Sataloff on prebyacousic sensitivity over the age of seventy; there is ground for pointing out, in fact, that it hardly corresponds to a general characteristic relationship; it is interesting however to note the parallel of the fall in sensitivity for frequencies 2,000 to 4,000 that class VII presents in respect to class IV. This

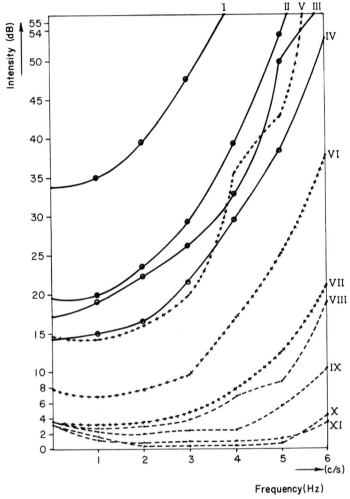

FIG. 26. See text (according to Dittrich and Fumeaux).

phenomenon could relate to a first phase of aging of the organ
of Corti between forty-forty-nine years.

We can note that in comparing the curves of presbyacousic
and traumatic sensitivities they have an analogous form and that
the second ones (in continuous lines) are found to be simply displaced in relation to the first ones (cruciform lines) on the scale
of intensities; the total value of each class is the same but dis-

placed in respect to age; thus a traumatic of forty years has a minimum threshold equivalent to a presbyacousic of 70. This important realization permits the conclusion that the *chronic professional sound traumatism* is in reality a phenomenon of prematured aging of the organ of Corti and not a traumatism, in the strict sense of the term, of the receptor organ. The term *chronic professional traumatism* thus does not correspond with a physiological reality.

In a first phase we have tried to adapt two analogous exponential functions (I and IV) to the experimental curve (II) (curve VI of Fig. 26), the first of form $y = A_e^{(x-a)^2}$ follows at first rather faithfully the experimental curve, separating itself from it by a sudden dip, steeper at point 3; the second, of form $y = Ae^{(x-a)}$ presents similar analogies but with, on the contrary, a strong inflexion toward the right at point 3. Calculations of approximation permit us to determine the value of the closest function (III) of the experimental curve (II) (separation $= 2$ p.c.).

We obtain respectively:

I   : $y = 6{,}9 \ e^{\ 0{,}116 \ (X-1{,}04)^2}$

IV   : $y = 6{,}62e^{\ 0{,}223 \ (X-0{,}782)}$

I   : $y = 6{,}9 \ e^{\ 0{,}151 \ (X-0{,}93)^{\frac{2}{3}}}$

Vertifications made for all the proposed curves permit the establishment of the general relationship:

$$Y = A_{e_2}^{\ \lambda(X-a)^{\mu_3}} \qquad (2.4.1)$$

of which the 4 parameters A, λ, a, μ determine the 4 fundamental properties of auditive sensitivity.

A $=$ general value of sensitivity in function of age,

a $\ =$ maximum sensitivity,

μ $=$ relative sensitivity of class,

λ $\ =$ relative sensitivity in function of frequencies.

An increase of A thus corresponds to a diminishing of the general auditive sensitivity (total and relative) and as a consequence causes the curve to rise on axis *y*.

An increase of *a* corresponds to a displacement of the threshold of maximum sensitivity toward the high tones and has as consequence the displacement of the maximum of the curve toward the right.

The parameters λ and μ vary in the same sense and determine the general steepness of the curve.   An increase in their value "flattens" the curve and modifies its opening.   Besides, it has a

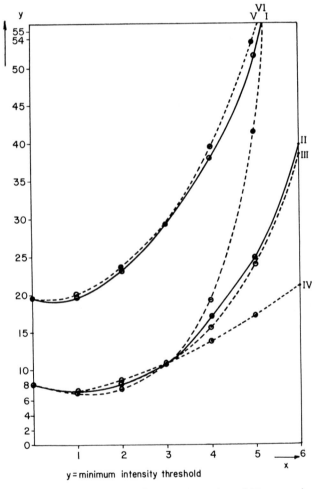

FIG. 27.   See text (according to Dittrich and Fumeaux).

corrective effect on A. It is interesting to be able to retain the same value for each class.

One can then, once these diverse data are established, make a comparative mathematical analysis of the presbyacousic and traumatic curves obtained for the most characteristic age classification (class VI). The graphic comparison (Fig. 27) of the two experimental curves (II and V) and their representative function (III and VI) can be put forth by the table (Fig. 28) demonstrat-

Presbyacousis (III)

X	(II) y exper.	(III) y funct.
0	7.91	7.91
1	6.91	7.05
2	8.16	8.16
3	10.58	10.7
4	17	15.0
5	24.91	24
6	40.16	38.7

$$A = 6.9$$
$$\lambda = 0.151$$
$$a = 0.93$$
$$\mu = \frac{3}{2}$$
$$y = 6.9\,e^{\,0.151\,(X-0.93)^{\frac{3}{2}}}$$

Traumatism c.p.s.t. (VI)

X	(V) y exper.	(VI) y funct.
0	19.4	19.3
1	19.8	19.4
2	23.4	23.02
3	29.2	29.2
4	29.8	38.
5	53.5	51.7
—	—	—

$$A = 18.9$$
$$\lambda = 0.1012$$
$$a = 0.37$$
$$\mu = \frac{3}{2}$$
$$y = 18.9\,e^{\,0.101\,(X-0.37)^{\frac{3}{2}}}$$

FIG. 28.   See text (according to Dittrich and Fumeaux).

ing in a peremptory fashion the mathematical validity of the conclusions we have previously reached.

The increase of A corresponds with a diminishing of the general sensitivity in function of age; we thus observe in the traumatic an "older" organ than in the ordinary presbyacousic.

The variation of λ is almost nonexistent; we notice, however, a
slight increase in the relative sensitivity to the high notes in
relation to the lower ones in the traumatic.

The perceptible diminishing of a signifies a displacement of the
maximum of sensitivity toward the low notes (240 c/s in presbya-
cousics as against 160 c/s for the same intensity in the traumatics).

The factor μ, relative sensitivity of class, is constant and equals $\frac{3}{2}$.

Lastly we can compare the values corresponding to x and y
for the experimental curves and the descriptive functions.   The
spread is an average of 2 p. c.   We can thus consider as pathological cases which separate significantly the curves thus established.

We have tried to show a general view of the actual position of
the Biophysics of Hearing but it is well known that in the future
several elements will be added, suppressed or corrected.

SECTION THREE

BIOPHYSICS OF ORIENTATION OR OF THE VESTIBULAR SYSTEM

INTRODUCTION

"We only know natural phenomena by their relation with causes that they produce."

(CL. BERNARD)

THE COMING OF wave mechanics has greatly contributed to the simplification of biophysical problems: the internal ear gives an excellent illustration. We have succeeded, in fact, in creating a new acoustic, that is to say *generalized;* we had overlooked for too long a time the fact that the *real direction of this scientific discipline lay in the use, by the cochleo-vestibulary ear and the brain, of vibrations of matter,* calling upon at the same time the science of vibrations, physiology and the theory of information. We realized at the same time how much the *study of the signal* would take away from that of other parameters, considered until now as basic elements.

ONDULATORY CINETICS AND VESTIBULARY MECHANICS

Sound waves are *vibrations of material media which transmit to each other* by degrees. Each material particle acts upon its neighbour transmitting to it the movement it possesses; one conceives, as has already been mentioned above, that the propagation of sound in a medium will depend on the *mechanic characteristics of the medium* as well as the *characteristics of the sound itself.* In the case of the ear, *what distinguishes the cochlear from the vestibular compartments is that the first is impressed by vibrations which are transmitted to it having an exterior source, while the second is impressed with vibrations which arise in its immediate neighborhood and of which the source is accidentally exterior to the anatomic limits which circumscribe it.*

It is important to underline in this connection the difference which exists between *transmitter* and *generator* of sounds. If we put aside high-frequency transmitters, usual transmitters consist of *vibratory systems communicating their vibrations to a surrounding medium* (sirens, whistles and vibrating pipes, vibrating cavities); sound generators are instruments of the *mechanic causality of the initiation and the maintaining of the vibration* (bow, periodically fed electromagnet, mechanical or thermic agitator of a solid, a liquid or a gas).

We have also mentioned above that sound is propagated in a *straight line* from the sonic source to the receiver; there thus exist, in a manner, sound rays which are analogous to light rays. This permits us, as we have seen, to define a speed of sound and a *sound wave* which materializes through a surface *(wave surface)* perpendicular to the direction of the sound. *We recall that the sound wave creates a pressure on a screen.* Remember too that we can calculate the value of the surface force of a wave (in Watts/cm^2); this value is the expression of the strength of sound on 1 cm^2 of the surface of the wave: it is inversely proportional to the square of the distance covered. We know too that for a sound of a given frequency the wavelength varies according to the medium of propagation in conformance with the formula $\lambda = vT$. Only the frequency is characteristic of a sound.

If we take the equation of the movement of a particle, $x = a \cos \omega E$ we call *intensity* of the movement quantity I:

$$I = a^2\omega^2 = 4\pi^2a^2v^2 \quad (3.2.1)$$

One rarely has the occasion to use it, but it should not be confused with the quantities that we are going to examine. (*I* will always be expressed in C.G.S. units, *a* in centimeters.)

We have seen how the transmission by degrees carries with it modifications of local pressure along the sound ray: at a given point there exists an overpressure variable in relation to the pressure which exists in the surrounding medium in the absence of sound. Let $\bar{\omega}$ be that over-pressure. It is conditioned by the movement of the material particle and will be ruled by a typical law:

$$\bar{\omega} = \bar{\omega}_m \cos \omega E \quad (3.2.2)$$

where $\bar{\omega}_m$ represents the maximum over-pressure possible in the course of the movement (the amplitude of the over-pressure) and ω is the pulsation of the sound. This law shows that the over-pressure is *at times positive,* when it is a true over-pressure; *at times negative:* this is a depression. It changes sign v times per second. The real pressure at the given point, at the instant E is, calling the surrounding pressure p, equal to $p + \bar{\omega}$. We call *acoustical pressure* $\bar{\omega}_m$: to distinguish it from *radiant pressure,* of which we will speak later on. *Acoustical pressure can deform a membrane which vibrates with the sound. The amplitude of the vibration of this loose resonator is translated electrically.* We thus have a microphone which serves both to measure the acoustical pressure and the intensity of the sound, in which case it functions in the manner of a transducer of energy. The comprehension of these physical phenomena is indispensable to that of the functioning of the ampullary cristae of the semicircular canals which constitute a particularly pertinent case of the complex resonator-transducer.

Since a material particle is animated by the movement
x = a cos ωE mechanics teaches us that at each instant it
possesses:

1) *a speed* u = −aω sin ωE. This speed varies with time
and changes v times per second; one can write out the law of its
variation in the form:

$$U = u_m \sin \omega E \quad (3.2.3)$$

showing the existence of a maximum speed u_m which can be
shown to be united to the maximum acoustical pressure $\bar{\omega}_m$ by the
relation: $\bar{\omega}_m = Ru_m$. In consequence, the law describing the
variation of acoustical pressure in function of time for a particle
under the law of movement a cos ωE is:

$$\bar{\omega} = - Ra \, \omega \sin \omega E \quad (3.2.4)$$

Remark that this law is in opposition of phase to that of movement, that is to say that, when the *displacement is maximum, the
pressure is non-existent.* This observance bears a particular importance in the study of modifications of cupular morphism during a stimulation and, while confirming the experimental results,
it shows the weakness of the ingenious hypothesis which is lacking in all realistic basis, the "pendulum of cupular torsion."

2) *an acceleration* g = −aω^2 cos ωE which varies according
to the same laws of which the importance is significant in the
production of certain secondary effects.

3) *a cinetic energy* (due to its speed) *and an energy potential*
(due to its pressure). These two energies are equal: the total
energy contained in the volume V of fluid is equal to their sum. Its
average value in a second is:

$$E = \frac{\rho V a^2 \omega^2}{2} \quad (3.2.5)$$

If the specific mass ρ is measured in grams/cc, the celerity V of
the wave or the speed *u* in centimeters/second, the amplitude *a*
in centimeters, *E* will be expressed in *ergs*. The practical unit of
energy being the *joule*, we find with this unit:

$$E = 5.10^{-8} \, \rho a^2 \omega^2 V \quad (3.2.6)$$

There corresponds to this energy a density of energy, energy contained in 1 cc of fluid, in *joules/cc*:

$$e = \frac{E}{V} = 5.10^{-8}\, \rho a^2 \omega^2 = 2.10^{-7} \pi^2 a^2 v^2 \quad (3.2.7)$$

which is proportional to the intensity of the sound:

$$e = 5.10^{-8}\, \rho I \quad (3.2.8)$$

The energy propagates itself with the celerity v along the sound ray. The density of energy, while possessing no physical nature, has the dimensions of a pressure: this comes in the difficult calculus of the pressure of radiation.

However, before introducing the notion of pressure of radiation, we must speak of the *acoustical strength of a sound fascicule*. By this must be understood the *surface strength W transported by the wave* due to the movement of the particles. We define it too as the energy per second on a surface of 1 cm²: the C.G.S. unit of acoustical strength is the erg/second/cm². Its calculation, which is easy, leads to the following expressions:

$$W = \tfrac{1}{2}\, \overline{\omega}_m\, u_m = \tfrac{1}{2}\, \overline{\omega}_m a \omega \quad (3.2.9)$$

where, bringing in the acoustical resistability, expressed in C.G.S. units and in using the Watt/cm² as the unit of surface strength:

$$W = 5.10^{-8}\, \frac{\overline{\omega}_m^2}{R} = 5.10^{-8} R u_m^2 = 2.10^{-7} \pi^2 R a^2 v^2 = 5.10^{-8} R I \quad (3.2.10)$$

It is also related to the density of energy by the formula:

$$W = ev \quad (3.2.11)$$

where v is in centimeter/second as is u_m, while $\overline{\omega}_m$ is in dynes/cm² or *microbars, a* in centimeters and *e* in joules/cc. These formulas show that

1) the surface strength is proportional to the square of the over pressure,
2) to the square of the amplitude of the vibration,
3) to the square of the frequency of the vibration,
4) to the vibratory intensity,
5) to the acoustical resistability of the medium.

These formulas are to be compared with those used in electricity in alternating or direct current but acoustical pressure takes the place of tension or the difference of potential; maximum speed (and not intensity I) of the vibration takes the place of the electrical intensity; acoustical resistability R plays in relation to the pressure and speed the same role that electrical resistance plays in relation to tension and electrical intensity.

Radiation pressure, as different from acoustical pressure, corresponds to an effect which is always exercised in the same direction (uni-directional effect). *Acoustical pressure* is an instantaneous over-pressure exerted in a fixed section of medium: variable with time, it has an average value of *zero* at all points. We can pick up by placing on the path of movement a membrane fixed at its edges (microphones, drum, ampullary cupula) which will participate in the movement. This fact explains that physiological acoustical measurements take into consideration only acoustical pressure. The particular case of the microphonic membrane of the posterior labyrinth, a case which has been very little considered up to now, obliges us to take into consideration also the radiation pressure of the endolymphatic fluid. We shall see the reasons for this.

Radiation pressure in a liquid is the average value of the over-pressure which is exerted in a section of fluid which follows the movement. It is always *positive,* and in the case which we will first consider, of a simple movement, it can not be zero. It can be measured with the aid of a manometer displacing itself with the fluid.

The existence of a radiation pressure is due to the fact that the propagation of the wave modifies the physical and mechanical properties of the fluid in the zones of compression and dilatation. In fact, ρ depends on the pressure, as does v, thus on the acoustical resistability. In an analagous manner, if in an electrical conductor for which the resistance varies in function of the intensity which traverses it, we pass an alternative current, we receive at the extremities a difference of alternative potential and, besides, a continuous component; the conductor is quite a rectifying device. The radiation pressure is exactly that continuous component which superposes itself on the static pressure of the fluid. In fact, the fluid perturbed by the wave has its modified state as a solid submitted to forces and having constraints or "tensions." It is this "radiation tension" which manifests its existance in rejecting a rigid obstacle (non-vibrating), mobile and reflective, which consists of the membraneous envelope of the labyrinth. Used to measure ultra-sounds, the radiation tension can naturally serve to measure the intensity of an ordinary sound fascicule without the intervention of an electrical current or a loose resonator (microphone) which always involve some distortions, or a gauge quartz. This measurement is fundamental in the establishment of a vestibulary model: it permits bringing out the true mechanical role of the membranes which occur in the solution of this biophysical problem. In fact, for very feeble strengths, radiation pressure is very difficult to use as it hardly lends itself to amplification; it is, moreover, much weaker than acoustical pressure.

Calculation of radiation tension is very delicate and brings in a quantity of the same nature as the density of energy. It is thus expressed in function of $d^2\omega^2$, d being the amplitude of *real* movement of a particle. If radiation pressure is called π, we have, with k as a coefficient of proportionality:

$$\pi = kd^2\omega^2 \quad (3.2.12)$$

in the case of a simple movement where $d = a$, the preceding formula is that of Lord Rayleigh:

$$\pi = \tfrac{1}{2}(\gamma+1) \frac{W}{v} = \tfrac{1}{2}(\gamma+1)e \quad (3.2.13)$$

When W is in ergs/second/cm^2 and v in cm/second, π is expressed in *microbars*. If the obstacle is totally absorbent of the sound, that is the pressure it supports (the case of the cupular membrane in orthomorphic position); if it is reflecting, it supports this incidental pressure *plus the reaction created by the sound energy it sends back*, designated by re, it is then submitted to the pressure:

$$\tfrac{1}{2}(\gamma+1)(e+re) = \pi(1+r) \quad (3.2.14)$$

r designating the coefficient of reflection.

An obstacle which is totally reflecting (the case of the cupular membrane in metamorphic position, at the limit of the rupture), $(r = 1)$ is submitted to a pressure double that withstood by an absorbent obstacle $(r = 0)$. Meanwhile, if the dimensions of the

obstacle are of the same order as the length of the wave, the
phenomena of diffraction complicates the law; besides, the flatness
of the obstacle renders the calculation still more difficult. These
facts explain in a certain measure why otophysiologists, even otophysicists, have been quite discouraged before this problem, of
which the least that can be said is that it is not a simple one to
resolve.

Radiation pressure is not isotropic, that is to say that in contrast
to ordinary pressures, it is not exercised in the same fashion in all
directions. If the sound ray makes an angle ϑ with the perpendicular at the screen, the radiation pressure supported by the screen is

$$\pi' = \pi \cos^2 \vartheta \quad (3.2.15)$$

This fact is added to the anisotropy of the cupular screen itself, a
fundamental element of which the "torsion pendulum" theory
takes no account. The reader can now form an idea of the complexity of a problem of which the data, scanty, it is true, are in-
tricately bound in a mathematical complex on a very high level.

The notion of real displacement d has a fundamental consequence in the order of stationary waves where we consider the
superposition of two movements of the same amplitude and the
same frequency being propagated in opposite directions. There
are then points (vibration nodes) where the movement is non-
existent whereas in others it is maximum (vibration loops). *The
radiation pressure is zero at the vibration nodes and maximum at
the loops* whereas in simple movement it is the same at all points.
On the other hand, the density of energy exists everywhere; it is
constant: the average value of the radiation pressure is equal to
it when $\gamma = 1$. Finally, the radiation pressure being proportional to the surface strength, thus to the square of the frequency,
it is natural that at equal amplitude of vibration, it can be very
weak for sounds and considerable for ultra-sounds. This is the
basis of the labyrinthic destructions due to ultra-sounds. It is
worth mentioning that it is also because the radiation pressure is
related to a density of energy, that the pressure exerted obliquely
is equal to $\pi \cos^2 \vartheta$; if it is calculated by considerations of pressure
and force, it is expressed in $\cos \theta$. This dependence on the direction translates an actual appearance in fluid of analogous forces

to the "tensions" existing in solids, which justifies the use of the term *radiation tension*. It is well known that as one goes further from the source, the amplitude of the vibratory state diminishes. Besides the weakening due to distance there are other causes of the diminishment related to the medium of propagation and the molecular friction in particular. We can say that there is an absorption of the sonic strength. In fact, supporting a parallel sound beam, the law of the squares of distances no longer comes in, and still the sound weakens. In a fluid, the amplitude at the distance d from the source is:

$$a = a_0 e^{-Kd} \quad (3.2.16)$$

a_0 being the amplitude at the height of the source, and e the base of the Neperian logarithms ($e = 2{,}718.28$); K represents the coefficient of absorption, calculated in the framework of the classic mechanic by Stokes-Kirchhoff and defined by:

$$K = B\eta v^2 + B' \propto^2 \chi v^2 \quad (3.2.17)$$

η is the viscosity; $\propto$ the coefficient of cubic dilatation at constant pressure, χ the thermic conductibility and v the frequency of the sound. The first term is a mechanic absorption K_{mec} by viscosity, the second $K_{Eh,}$ an heat absorption by heat transfer to the neighbouring particles. We see, consequently, that a sound is absorbed better as:

1) *its frequency is greater*
2) the celerity is weaker
3) the specific mass of the medium is weaker
4) the viscosity is greater.

Since the surface strength is proportional to the square of the amplitude, it will decrease too according to the law: $W = W_0 e^{-2Kd}$ where W_0 designates the initial strength. We can translate this law into weakening decibels; the number a of these decibels is

$$a = 10 \log \frac{W_0}{W} \quad (3.2.18)$$

from which:

$$a = 8{,}6878.Kd \quad (3.2.19)$$

This expression is only valid in the case of a parallel beam. When it is a question of non-radiated sounds in all space, the beam is divergent and the waves spheric: there is thus besides weakening of the vibration by this removal according to the law of the inverse of squares of distances. These notions bear a particular importance in the determination and in the explanation of differential sensitivities of the labyrinthic medium. In fact, fitting perfectly into the framework of generalized acoustics, it has been possible to introduce measures enfeebling sonic strength to a degree of preliminary value relative to the cochleo-vestibulary system; it is in this way that we have been able to situate the least sensitive threshold of the cochlea at about 80 decibels above the most sensitive threshold, whereas the least sensitive threshold of the posterior labyrinth is found at about 300 decibels above its least most sensitive threshold, in such a way that we can say that *where the sensitivity of the cochlea ends that of the vestibulum begins.*

The sound transfer takes place in both compartments of the ear by a propagation through different media. On this subject we have spoken, in the second part of this work, of the notion of acoustical impedance; we shall not go into the question again here. In fact, in the posterior labyrinth, the ondulatory propagation from one medium to another is in a way a final stage of excitation, since the waves ordinarily arise in the immediate neighbourhood of the resonator-transducer screen, that is to say in the intimity of the anatomic structures themselves. We have already stressed the difference which exists in this connection between the vestibulum and the cochlea, concerning which the stimulatory vibrations come from an exterior source at the anatomical limits which pick up its qualities. This state of things allows our adding a subsidiiary consideration, which is not without importance, on the respective sensitivity of the two compartments: we can say, adopting a word used in telecommunications, that the cochlea is quasi-insensitive to its "background noise," for which the level is very far from its inferior level sensitivity; the vestibulum, on the contrary, seems to possess in this case values much closer to these two ondulatory components. In a word, its sensitivity is extremely great, contrary to the opinion of many authors who have long seen in it the crudest of sensorial receptors.

An important particular case of propagation from one media to another is that of the *impedance adaptors,* of which we have already spoken, on the subject, of sound transmission by the ossicles. Such a particular case arises also in the posterior labyrinth in the endolymphatic cupular vibratory transmission; it is easy to imagine that the fidelity and the reproducability, for a rigourously reproducable stimulus itself, of impulses received, constitutes the only guarantee of normal and rational functioning of the sense of orientation. There is no need to describe a world in which, in the normal state of things, the sensorial receptors of a given subject respond in a different manner each time to the same stimulus; this is the world of the absurd, where all reference values are abolished. The impedance adaptor furnishes, within the limits of exigible tolerance, the necessary guarantees, in the normal state, of this reproducability. If the sound ray is perpendicular to the surface of separation of the two media, that is to say if the sound wave is parallel to the surface, we designate by W_i the incidental surface strength, W_r the reflected strength and W_r' the refracted strength. The interfacial reflective power is defined by

$$r = \frac{W_r}{W_i} \quad (3.2.20)$$

relation of the reflected strength and the incidental strength. The calculation shows that:

$$r = \left(\frac{m-1}{m+1}\right)^2 \quad (3.2.21)$$

If we call t the transmission power, $t = 1 - r$:

$$\frac{W_r'}{W_i} = \frac{4m}{(m+1)^2} \quad \text{and for } m = \frac{R_2}{R_1} \quad (3.2.22)$$

Strictly, we must consider the impedance, but here it is confused with the resistiveness and the reflective power does not depend on the frequency. We thus calculate the reflective power for a sound going from *one* to *two:*

$$r = \left(\frac{R_2 - R_1}{R_1 + R_2}\right)^2 \quad \text{and } t = \frac{4\,R_1 R_2}{(R_1 + R_2)^2} \quad (3.2.23)$$

These expressions are symmetric in R_1 and R_2 and the reflective power of the interface remains the same if the sound comes from *two*; this power is thus *characteristic of the interface*. This is an analogous expression to that which we find in optics for the transmission and the reflection of light strength at the interface of two media: the acoustical resistance is there replaced by the index of refraction. Thus a perfectly reflecting surface will have a reflecting power equal to one. In such a case, it is necessary that the resistivities be very different ones from the other: we can then disregard one before the other and r will have the value R_1/R_1 or R_2/R_2. As to the coefficient of transmission, it is four times the relation of the resistivities, the greatest being in the denominator. These results are not found, however, in the other parameters. Thus if a_i is the amplitude of the incidental movement, that the reflected one is $a_r = \dfrac{m-1}{m+1} a_i$, that of the refracted one is

$a'_r = \dfrac{2}{m+1} a_i$ (it is a very weak fraction of the incidental amplitude). The same is true for speeds u. But if $\bar{\omega}_i$ is the incidental over-pressure, the reflected over-pressure is $\bar{\omega}_r = \dfrac{m-1}{m+1} \bar{\omega}_i$ (it is

equal to it), whereas that refracted is $\omega_r = \dfrac{2m}{m+1} \bar{\omega}_m$ (it is

double to the incidental overpressure if the resistivity of medium *two* is very much greater than that of medium *one*, almost zero when the opposite is the case). In fact, calculated reflection coefficients are not the only characteristic of the interface. Other factors can modify them very profoundly. The theory is only relative:

    1) To pure and homogeneous media; heterogeneous qualities increase considerably the reflective power. It is this latter case that exists in the study of the cupula-endolymph system.

    2) To indefinite media. If the medium *two* has a finite thickness (which is the case in the system we are considering), it is the plate which it constitutes that has the reflective power and not its surface of separation.

This axiom contradicts, at first sight, that mentioned above in the case of the cupular crista. In reality, the "plate" spoken of in this sense is virtual; the real limit of the ampullar crista is not a barrier of interdependent and stratified cells, but an electrical barrier. We must therefore consider both aspects of the interface, by finding an intermediary term.

In optics, the theory of the passage from one media to another of electromagnetic vibrations is quite analogous: the role of acoustical resistivity, we have said previously, is held there by the index of refraction. As the variations of the index are less considerable, for transparent media, than variations of acoustical resistivity, the coefficient of reflection (equal to unity for metals) is very weak for transparent media. An attempt can be made to diminish it still more by intercalating a third medium between the two, of intermediary index and very low density: we know that the optimum is reached by a thickness equal to a quarter of the wavelength of the light in the layer of passage, for then the reflected wave on the face of medium *one*, the passage layer, interferes with the reflected wave on the interface layer of passage, medium *two*, which is behind it by a half wavelength. This system would be applicable in acoustics. But the problem which presents itself most often is the determination of the coefficient of reflection of a thin plate which has a thickness e, acoustical resistivity R_2, immerged in a medium of acoustical resistivity R_1, which bathes both faces. The acoustical vibration is partially reflected by the plate, the remaining energy passing to the other side. The theory and the calculation show that:

1) when the thickness of the plate is little (about $\lambda/100$) the reflection coefficient is non-existent: the plate is transparent.

2) when the thickness of the plate increases, the reflection coefficient also increases, passes through a maximum near the value it would attain if the thickness of the plate was infinite for $e = \lambda/4$ (plate "one-quarter wave") then diminishes and disappears (the plate is transparent) when $e = \lambda/2$.

Thus, if we desire a perfect transmission, we have the choice between the use of a plate which is ultra-thin (very little solid) or a more resistant half-wave plate. This conclusion motivates the reservations we made above as to the conception of "plate" or interface. These reservations find their explanation in an adaptor of impedance system. The preceding limitation of validity, in function of the thickness of the medium, goes as well for the area of the interface, and the formulas applicable are only valid if it is unlimited or quite great. When it is small before the wavelength, the phenomena are perturbed. We are thus led to conceive of apparatuses, impedance adaptors, which permit a vibration to pass from medium *one* to medium *two* without reflection for values very different from the impedances. The simplest expression of such an apparatus can be summarized thus: the sound arriving on the transmission coming from medium *one* acts on a piston which, through the intermediary of a lever, activates another piston which causes medium *two* to vibrate. As we have already said, we have recognized in this system a mode of transmission which is analogous to that of the ossicles of the middle ear. We can calculate the characteristics of a perfect adaptor in function of resistivities: the system of pistons and levers will vibrate at the frequency of the sound and the transmission will vary with the frequency because of the inertia of the system; it will, besides, introduce distortions. We can thus trace, in function of the frequency, a curve representing the variation of the transmission. It is evident that an adaptor corresponding to the very schematic description above would not suit the endolymphatic-cupular system: if one could possibly transpose the pistons, where then would the levers be established? Experimentation shows however that such an adaptor undeniably exists; we must thus try to give as clear a representation of it as possible. The reader will pardon us for coming back to the general theory of *lines* here with all the mathematical baggage involved. It is first necessary to refer to the hyperbolic representation of a chain of quadripoles: if this chain consists of *n* reciprocal and symmetrical elements, we obtain the following relation between the operation sizes of entry and the sizes of exit:

$$\left\{ \begin{array}{c} U_e \\ I_e \end{array} \right\} = \left\{ \begin{array}{cc} \text{ch n } \vartheta & z_i \text{ sh n } \vartheta \\ \dfrac{\text{sh n } \vartheta}{z_i} & \text{ch n } \vartheta \end{array} \right\} \cdot \left\{ \begin{array}{c} U_s \\ I_s \end{array} \right\} \qquad (3.2.24)$$

ϑ here expressing the image exponent, furnishing in all cases a simple relation between the impedance at entry and the impedance at exit, the formula above being obtained starting from the chain matrix of the reciprocal and symmetrical quadripole. Let us suppose that n tends toward the infinite, that is that the chain will consist of a very great number of identical quadripoles, very small; n will then be a quantity proportional to the length x of the segment of line and we will have:

$$n\vartheta = \gamma x \qquad (3.2.25)$$

γ being the exponent of transfer ϑ for a number of elements equal to the unity of the length which, for this reason, we will call the exponent of linear tranfer. In this way the elementary quadripole has been replaced by an entity susceptible to being delivered on any length and represents a macroscopic quadripole characterized by a chain matrix, the function of its length. Such a situation re-occurs when the integration of a transformer series gives still another transformer, this summation of effects being a model of a particular composition of which we know several important examples: electrical lines or sound tubes of which the elements are quite as many elementary quadripoles. We must justify the apparent confusion which we have allowed in designating under the term of quadripole a transformer and simple line element: actually, in disposing a line of given characteristics between a source and a receptor, one acts very largely on the apparent impedance offered at that source, this being the fundamental property of the transformer; one can even show that a line of inferior dimension to a quarter of a wavelength acts indeed as a transformer lowerer or raiser of tension. Having thus established the matrix relation:

$$\left\{ \begin{array}{c} U_x \\ I_x \end{array} \right\} = \left\{ \begin{array}{cc} \text{ch}\gamma x & z_i \text{ sh } \gamma x \\ \dfrac{\text{sh}\gamma x}{z_i} & \text{ch}\gamma x \end{array} \right\} \cdot \left\{ \begin{array}{c} U_o \\ I_o \end{array} \right\} \qquad (3.2.26)$$

x being the distance of a certain section from the line to the receptor, whereas the same relation written between the receptor and a
slice of an absciss $x + \delta x$ will be

$$\left\{ \begin{matrix} U_{x+\delta x} \\ I_{x+\delta x} \end{matrix} \right\} = \left(\begin{matrix} \text{ch}\gamma(x+\delta x) & Z_1 \text{sh}\gamma(x+\delta x) \\ \dfrac{\text{sh}\gamma(x+\delta x)}{Z_i} & \text{ch}\gamma(x+\delta x) \end{matrix} \right) \cdot \left\{ \begin{matrix} U_o \\ I_o \end{matrix} \right\} \quad (3.2.27)$$

We thus deduce the following expressions:

$$\begin{aligned} U_{x+\delta x} &= U_o \text{ch}\gamma(x+\delta x) + I_o Z_1 \text{sh}\,\gamma\,(x+\delta x) \\ U_x &= U_o \text{ch}\gamma x \quad\quad\quad + I_o Z_1 \text{sh}\gamma\,(\delta x) \end{aligned} \quad (3.2.28)$$

that is to say that in making δx tend toward zero and in posing
$\delta U = U_{x+\delta x} - U_x$ we have $\delta U = I_o Z_i \gamma \delta x$ (3.2.29)
From which we have the fundamental relations:

$$\frac{dU}{dx} = I_o Z_i \gamma$$

$$\frac{dI}{dx} = \frac{\gamma}{Z_i} U \quad (3.2.30)$$

which gives the equations:

$$\frac{d^2 U}{dx^2} - \gamma^2\, U = O$$

$$\frac{d^2 I}{dx^2} - \gamma^2\, I = O \quad (3.2.31)$$

These equations are the image in plan p (Laplace-Heaviside transformation) of classic equations of vibrating cords. Put another
way, these, all those which follow from them, are found written
except for the single hypothesis of a line considered as a chain of
perfect systems, without falling back, as most otophysicists do,
on a more or less important series of sometimes wobbly analogies.
We said above that the line is in fact a transformer of impedances.
We will thus consider a line of x length, closed at its extremity by
a certain impedance Z_o ; it is seen from the entry under the impedance Z defined as for all quadripoles by the expression:

$$Z = \frac{Z_o \text{ch}\gamma x + Z_i \text{sh}\gamma x}{\dfrac{Z_o \text{sh}\gamma x + \text{ch}\gamma x}{Z_i}} \quad (3.2.32)$$

which is also written, putting $Z_o/Z_i = \text{Eh}\varphi$:

$$z = \text{th}\,(\gamma x + \varphi) \quad (3.2.33)$$

Such is the relation which permits the determination, in function of y and x, the impedance on which one must close the line in order that it has a given value at the entry. In particular we see that $\underline{Z}$ will have the same value, that is to say that the source is unaware that the receptor moves on the line if its distance x verifies the condition that $yx+\varphi$ are equal to a certain complex constant. But to pass from the "mechanical" adaptor with levers and pistons to the line, transformer of impedances, which will be the compromise (experimental, by the way) of the "plate-inter-face" block of the cupular-endolymphatic system, it is necessary to go a bit further. For this we must make explicit the quanti-ties $\underline{Z}_i$ and y in function of coefficients of the line if we define as the unity of the line an inductance L and a resistance R, whereas we will also admit a capacity C and a resistance of loss G, on the other side. These different measurable quantities have been es-tablished by electrophysiologists. The schema equivalent to an element of length represents a cell with the form of an L, the im-pedance in series in the line being $(Lp+R)\,\delta x$ and the impedance in parallel $(Cp+G)\delta x$. In these conditions the identification with the following expressions (see formula 3.2.30) which have served to establish the fundamental relations:

$$\delta U = I\underline{Z}_i\gamma\delta x$$

$$\delta I = \frac{\gamma}{\underline{Z}_i}\,U\delta x$$

give the relations:

$$Lp+R = \underline{Z}_i\gamma$$
$$Cp+G = \frac{\gamma^2}{\underline{Z}_i} \quad (3.2.34)$$

from which we deduce didrectly:

$$\gamma^2 = (Lp+R)\ (Cp+G) \quad (3.2.35)$$

and

$$\underline{Z}_i^2 = \frac{Lp+R}{Cp+G} \quad (3.2.36)$$

In the particular case of a sinusoidal excitation, the following remarks become obvious:

1) γ is real if $L = C = O$, that is in the case of a line having as a result of resistances, losses and faults of iso-

lation, but lacking inductance and capacity. z_i is then also a real quantity.

2) γ is purely imaginary if $R = G = O$, that is in the case of the line without loss. In this case $\gamma = j\sqrt{LC}$, whereas z_i is still a real quantity.

3) Finally, in the case where $L = G = O$, that is of a line having only resistance and capacity, we have $\gamma^2 = j$ $RC\omega$ from which $\gamma = \sqrt{\tfrac{1}{2}RC\omega}\,(1+j)$.

Let us note, besides that in the remarkable case where we have $L/C = R/G$, one of the relations deduced directly above shows that z_i is independently of p and in particular of pulsation in a sinusoidal regime. (We know that impedance images, in the case of reciprocal and symmetrical quadripoles—equal in absolute value—are confused with the iterative impedance z_i.) We can then take up the study of two fundamental cases begun before: the case where factor $th\gamma x$ will be infinite or nonexistent.

In case where $th\gamma x = \infty$ that is $ch\gamma x = 0$, the chain matrix of the line is reduced to:

$$T = \left\{ \begin{matrix} 0 & j z_i \\ \dfrac{j}{z_i} & 0 \end{matrix} \right\} \quad (3.2.37)$$

In fact, $ch\gamma x = 0$ leads to $sh\gamma x = j$ realization of the relation $ch^2\gamma x - sh^2\gamma x = 1$. In this case, the impedance of the closing z_0 is transformed into:

$$z = \frac{z_i^2}{z_0} \quad (3.2.38)$$

The element of the line acts as an inverser of impedances. In particular if $z_0 = 0$, z is infinite, or, if one is dealing with a line of length x such that $ch\gamma x = 0$, in short circuit at its extremity, it acts vis-a-vis, the source branched at the origin as if it functioned in open circuit (and vice-versa). The resolution of the equation $ch\gamma x = 0$ can be made by posing: $\gamma = \alpha + \beta j$. The equation thus becomes:

$$jth\,\alpha\,x = -cotg\beta\,x \quad (3.2.39)$$

α and β before being real numbers, the only solution will be:

$$\alpha = 0$$
$$\beta x = \kappa\pi + \pi/2 \quad (3.2.40)$$

that is that γ must be a purely imaginary number. Such a circumstance occurs, as we have said, with the line without loss for which in sinusoidal regime we know that: $\gamma = j\omega\sqrt{LC}$ (3.2.41) and the equation $ch\gamma x = 0$ sums up in these conditions:

$$\omega x \sqrt{LC} = \kappa\pi + \pi/2 \quad (3.2.42)$$

k being any whole number. Making, under the circumstances $k = 1$, there results

$$x = \frac{\pi}{2\omega\sqrt{LC}} \quad (3.2.43)$$

either by replacing w by $2\pi/T$ and in designating under the name of wavelength the product λ of T by $1/\sqrt{LC}$ (which has the dimensions of a length, the second term representing a speed of propagation):

$$x = \tfrac{1}{4}\lambda \quad (3.2.44)$$

whereas the other values of k give us in a general manner

$$x = \tfrac{1}{2}k\lambda + \tfrac{1}{4}\lambda \quad (3.2.45)$$

We find ourselves in the case of quarter wavelengths to which we referred in another context. But, as we have just seen, we are participating in the demonstration, not of an adaptor, but of an inverser of impedances. To find a coordination between experimentation and theory, we must examine the second possible case, that where $th\gamma x = 0$, that is $sh\gamma x = 0$.

The chain matrix of the line is then of the form:

$$\mathbf{T} = \begin{Bmatrix} -1 & 0 \\ 0 & 1 \end{Bmatrix} \quad (3.2.46)$$

and the impedance of closing $\mathcal{Z}_o$ is transformed into:

$$\mathcal{Z} = -\mathcal{Z}_o \quad (3.2.47)$$

that is to say that the source is in open circuit or in short circuit according to whether at this distance x such that $sh\gamma x = 0$, the line is itself in open circuit or in short circuit. The solution of the equation is obtained too by supposing $\gamma = \propto + \beta j$ which gives:

$$th \propto x + j \, tg\beta x = 0 \quad (3.2.48)$$

an equation of which the solution, in $\propto$ and β is:

$$\propto = 0$$
$$\beta x = j\kappa\pi \quad (3.2.49)$$

There again, we conclude that the hypothesis put forward only concerns the line without loss of which the length x will be of the form:

$$x = \kappa\lambda + \tfrac{1}{2}\lambda \quad (3.2.50)$$

this discussion completing the preceding one.

Outside of these particular cases, it appears that in the general case $\underline{Z}$ will be a complex function of $\underline{Z}_0$. But then independently of a $th\gamma x$ nonexistent or infinite, the equation (see form 3.2.36) permits the reaching of a general result which is very important and valid for any $th\gamma x$, or for a line without loss of any length, x. It is the question of the hypothesis where that line, regardless of its length, closes on a purely reactive impedance. In this case its impedance of entry is also purely reactive. Let us actually consider that we have

$$\underline{Z}_0 = Lp \quad (\text{or } \underline{Z}_0 = \frac{1}{CP}) \quad (3.2.51)$$

we note that the quotient $\underline{Z}_0/\underline{Z}_i$ is a purely imaginary number and $\underline{Z}$ becomes in sinusoidal regime

$$\underline{Z} = j\frac{L\omega \; \cos\,(2\pi x/\lambda) + \sqrt{L/C}\,\sin\,(2\pi x/\lambda)}{\cos\,(2\pi x/\lambda) - C\omega\,\sin\,(2\pi x/\lambda)} \quad (3.2.52)$$

That is $\underline{Z}$ is also a purely reactive impedance, which can be explained in the cupular-endolymphatic system by considerations of energy. The notion of line transformer is thus very interesting, not only for the study of phenomena starting at their source but also to analyse the process of transformation of impedances with all the *adaptations* which can result.

The nature of phenomena arising in the line itself implies the necessity of considering the equation of propagation (see form 3.2.31) of which the integration is immediate:

$$U(x) = U_1 e^{\gamma x} + U_2 e^{-\gamma x} \quad (3.2.53)$$

and

$$I(x) = \frac{U_1}{\underline{Z}_i} e^{\gamma x} - \frac{U_2}{\underline{Z}_i} e^{-\gamma x} \quad (3.2.54)$$

We express in the two equations above $x = 0$, by thus being put at the extremity of the line, where the receptor possibly could be.

We call U_o and I_o the sizes of the entry of this receptor. It follows that:

$$U_o = U_1 + U_2$$
$$I_o Z_i = U_1 - U_2 \quad (3.2.55)$$

These relations permit the expression of U_1 and U_2 in function of U_o, I_o and Z_i. But at the same time a very important piece of information is revealed, that is that from the moment that these quantities U_1 and U_2 are determined in a certain way by the receptor, we must consider the existence of two currents actually translating an exchange in the direction of source receptor and in the opposite direction. U consists in fact of two terms which translate respectively an incidental wave and a reflected wave.

When the entirely reflected wave turns backward it hits the incidental wave. A molecule will obey, in its movement, the incidental wave and the reflected wave. There will thus exist in some regions of space where these movements will be added at each instant, and others where they will compensate each other exactly. We referred to this above in undertaking the role of phase displacement of two waves. In space regions such as A and B regularly spaced at a half wavelength, the displacement of molecules is nil, but the over-pressure is maximum (pressure loop, displacement node); at a point situated at mid-distance, we have, on the contrary a loop of displacement and a pressure node. These privileged regions are well defined and form a system called stationary waves. Their name is due to the fact that movement is not propagated: at the displacement nodes (or vibration nodes) the particles remain at rest; at the loops, the particles vibrate, but their neighbours vibrate with a lesser amplitude. The position of the loops and nodes does not vary with time. Without going once more into the detail of the theory of stationary waves, we would insist upon the acceptance of their use in the creation of a vestibular model; using india ink or a ludion stopping at the nodes, we can measure by application of the formula $\lambda = vT$: the celerity of the vibrations of the medium, knowing the frequency of these vibrations, on the one hand, and also the range of frequencies possible by the vibration in the medium of which we know the characteristics.

We have seen that with the exception of sirens, a sound system which is excited is capable of transmitting a pure sound. We come back once and for all to the fact that the terms "sound" and "sonic" and in general all that is classed under "acoustics" must not be understood in the restrictive sense which it has until now been attributed to it. In fact, besides the sounds which translate periodic movements, it would be fitting to consider the transitory phenomena corresponding to the pneumatic transmissions. Pneumatic science is thus for acoustics the replica in electricity of any currents opposed to sinusoidal currents. We can thus define, as we already have done, generalized notions (acoustical inductance, acoustical resistance, acoustical capacity), regardless of the nature of the movement.

A pure sound, also called *fundamental,* of frequency v_0 , this frequency being related to the physical or geometrical properties of the transmitter and called for this reason *fundamental frequency of resonance,* will develop a great intensity in consideration of the exciting cause. One can, by various artifices, compel the transmitter to transmit on a frequency v different from v_0 : one then has forced vibrations for which the intensity will be very weak. A notable intensity (in general lower than the fundamental) can be obtained in exciting the transmitter to the frequency of $2v_0$ (2nd harmonic) and so on. Keep in mind that the transmitter resounds well on its fundamental frequency and on the harmonics of it. Even so, the intensity will be weak on the high harmonics. We know that these considerations are purely theoretical, since a transmitter does not transmit pure sounds but complex sounds, consisting of the fundamental and the first harmonics, or partial in general much weaker. These phenomena are particularly clear and bear a great practical importance therefore, for cords, stems and vibrating cavities as well as for certain electrical structures. We call them *resonators.*

An incomplete interpretation of the experimental data as well as an immoderate affection for analogy—these are the principal factors in the hesitant nature of vestibulary otophysiological research during many years; numerous authors gave up just before reaching the goal. They were led to attributing to the ampullary cupula the properties of a pendulum which is greatly damped out, properties quite close to its real properties of a resonator, but which lead to error. If we consider the effect of the response of a resonator to a unique excitation, we notice that the vibratory movement adopted is described by the equation:

$$x = Ae^{-BE} \cos 2\pi v_o E \quad (3.2.56)$$

where x is the elongation of its movement (*which is translated by the intensity* of the vibrations), A, a constant of proportionality, e the base of the neperian logarithms, B, a constant which depends on the characteristics of the resonator, E, the time, v_o, the frequency proper to the resonator.

This equation expresses that the movement of the resonator is almost periodic (from period $T_o = 1/v_o$) and that it deadens according to the exponential law e^{-BE}, that is to say, it tends toward zero more rapidly as B is greater. B is the coefficient of deadening and a resonator is that much more deadened as its coefficient of deadening is raised. The constant A depends closely on the cause that has set off the movement of the resonator and it is naturally greater as the cause is more important. The time $\gamma = 1/B$ at the end of which the amplitude has become A/e is the *time constant*. It is sufficient to remember that a resonator but little deadened makes its own frequency heard much longer if the excitation is of short duration. We can express the importance of the deadening in function of the logarithmic decrement δ defined in the following manner:

$$\delta = BT_o \quad (3.2.57)$$

If the deadening is great, the decrement is important; if the resonator is very little deadened, δ is weak. The logarithmic decrement is about constant for all the frequencies and characterizes the material of which the resonator is made. If B_o designates more precisely the coefficient of deadening at the frequency of resonance and B_h the coefficient at the frequency hv_o:

$$\delta = B_o/v_o = B_h/hv_o \quad (3.2.58)$$

thus $B_h = hB_o$ and the deadening increases with the harmonic order. Consequently, at great frequencies (T_o little) the deadening will be considerable. Sometimes the logarithmic decrement is replaced by the factor of quality Q, also characteristic of the material:

$$Q = \pi/\delta \quad (3.2.59)$$

To come back to the problem which preoccupies us, let us say that the experimental conditions with their direct effects (modification of the cupulary morphism) and indirect effects (occulary nystagmus), conditions verified by the theoretical considerations which precede, place the cupulary resonator, for which the logarithmic decrement is weak, among the resonators which are but little deadened. This quality is made even more evident at the time of the response of a resonator to a sinusoidal excitation. Thus, if the resonator is excited by a cause of frequency v: a cos $2\pi vE$ it takes the movement:

$$x = Ae^{-BE} \cos 2\pi v_0 E + C \cos 2\pi vE \quad (3.2.60)$$

The first part of the equation indicates that it reacts to the excitation in a personal manner (which is the case of the cupular resonator). This movement disappears more or less quickly, according to the deadening B of the resonator, and constitutes the transitory regime. A depends naturally on the amplitude a of the exciting cause (the DeVries chair, for example). *The second part indicates that the resonator takes a regime of oscillation of frequency identical to the excitation* (which is also the case of the cupular resonator considered in its indirect nystagmic effect and, until further inquiry, in its direct metamorphic state: continuous vibratory state of the plate interface or line). *This regime does not lessen and lasts as long as the exciting cause.* The discussion of two secondary phenomena must enter in at this point. The first is that of a supposed fatigability of the vestibulary apparatus: as for the cochlear ear, there is reason for not confusing here the neuro-sensorial phenomena, subject to a "physiological" fatigability and the physical phenomena (vibratory regime) which, depending only on the duration and the intensity of the stimulus, follow faithfully the stimulus without submitting to fatigability. The second is that certain corrections must be made on this ideal resonator for it to be analogous to the cupular resonator: one of these corrections which is essential resides in the fact of considering, as we will farther on, the dissymmetry of its reactions. The

non-deadened regime, lasting as long as the exciting cause, constitutes, by opposition to precedent, a permanent regime or yet a
regime of forced oscillations. We can consider that this permanent regime is the normal mode of oscillation, perturbed by the
transitory regime. In current practice it is permissable to discount
the latter which has a negligable amplitude after a very short
time in relation to the duration of the action of the permanent
cause. In this connection, it is fitting to put a finger on an apparent paradox, that of the duration we call "physiological" of the
orientative stimulus (rotation of head in everyday life) and that
of the "clinical" duration of the explorative stimulus of the orientative function: in reality, this paradox is only one for those who
cannot conceive of a systematic exploration, so that the search for
a threshold of excitability calls for, by reason of its recording an
analytical "slowdown," which synthesized, restores perfectly the
conditions called physiological. In fact, there is only need for
being concerned with the value of C, which depends:

1. On a, that is to say on the greatness of the amplitude
   of the periodic cause exciting the resonator, an important cause obviously inducing forced oscillations of
   great amplitude. It is, mark well, on this property
   that we base the measure the acoustical pressure with
   the help of a transducter, that is, a resonator, loose or
   harmonized, which transforms the mechanical vibrations which it takes, coming from the oscillatory regime
   into electrical vibrations (alternate current) of the
   same frequency as the excitatory vibration and susceptible to amplification. There is no better way of
   describing biophysically the cupular mechanism. If
   the resonator is loose, it can, with more or less fidelity,
   reproduce complex sound; we know that if it is harmonized, it only responds to sinusoidal vibrations at
   its own frequency.
2. On the difference between frequencies v_0 and v.
3. On the deadening B of the resonator.

In fact, the amplitude C of the forced oscillations is greater as
the frequency v_0 of the resonator itself and the frequency v

of the excitation are close. In other terms C is weak if v is less than $v/2$ or more than $3/2v$, it passes through a maximum for $v = v_0$ (then there is *resonance*) but it also depends on B and we then have to consider two cases:

A.—and it is the case of the cupula—the resonator is very slightly deadened (little B). The permanent regime is not stable, C increases very quickly when v comes closer to v_0 and can reach the resonance of very great value, out of proportion with the amplitude of the exciting cause. This value, uncomfortable for the ear, can be dangerous to the resonator itself and bring on its destruction (in the case of the cupula, its temporary or definitive rupture). On the other hand, the resonator is *very selective*: it only responds if the exciting vibration corresponds to a fundamental sound (or to the first harmonics, but with a very slight amplitude). It will not resound for very close frequencies (shrill resonance). In fact, if x_0 is the amplitude of the movement to the resonance (frequency v_0), we define the acuity of resonance by seeking the frequency v for which the amplitude becomes $x_0/\sqrt{2}$. The calculation shows that the acuity is given with this formula:

$$\frac{v-v_0}{v_0} = \pm \frac{\delta}{2\pi} \quad \text{(For δ little)} \quad (3.2.61)$$

where δ is the logarithmic decrement of the resonator. If the resonance is very sharp, v will be only slightly different from v_0. δ will be then extremely small and the sharp resonance is the attribute of resonators with small logarithmic decrements, thus very little deadened. We can note that $v - v_0 = \pm B/2\pi$ or even that the acuity is inversely proportional to the time constant. A very selective resonator only responds to a very small number of frequencies, but it can detect extremely weak amplitudes, which constitutes one of the fundamental qualities of the sense of orientation.

It is fitting to remark that, even harmonized, a resonator does not instantaneously take its regime amplitude. For this it needs a certain amount of time when, in short, some impulses will not be caught. We had previously rendered an account of these phenomena starting with the experimental fact that the cupula is orthomorphic for the infra-liminary values of the Rotating Liminary Test according to Montandon, verifying that this "state of rest" results in an absence of vestibulary nystagmic reaction on the electronystagmographic graph; starting, on the other hand, with the experimental fact that the frequency of nerve influx recorded at the level of the vestibulary nerve is proportionally increased with the compression of the cupula and consequently proportionally increased with the stimulus of rotatory acceleration (as long as the latter does not constitute, as the result of a high or irregular value, a cause of resonance of rupture), adding to these indirect effects, the direct study, image by image, of the cupulary metamorphism in function of time under the effect of diverse classic stimulations—study which until now has been conducted only on animals for reasons easily understood—we have been able to determine that the metamorphism of the cupula in function of time could at most be described by a differential equation of the type:

$$\sum_{k=0}^{n} a_K \frac{d^k y}{dt^k} = 0 \quad (3.2.62)$$

of which the form $y(t) = \sum_{k=1}^{n} A_k e^{\gamma_k t}$, allows the determination of the stability or instability of the system. This equation had the advantage of requiring less individual parameters (A_K representing the constants of integration determined by the initial conditions and γ_K representing the roots of the equation characteristic of the differential equation) than differential equations presented to account for the same phenomena; the greater number of them also having the disadvantage of a fundamental error which consists in seeing in the metamorphism an actual movement (torsion pendulum) and not a simple deformation of membrane due to the systems of waves of compression consecutive to the rotatory stimulus.

B. The second case, which we consider only as an antithesis, and therefore only briefly, is that of the *very deadened* resonator. The amplitude C remains weak, but the resonator is capable of responding almost equally to very different frequencies from the fundamental. It is slightly selective and the resonance is called loose. As an example, take the tune fork immersed in water; a

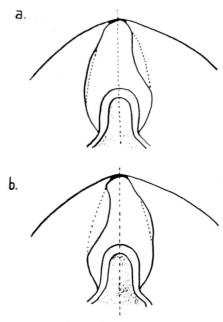

Fɪɢ. 29. Cupulary metamorphism during rotation, observed by Steinhausen in the pike. (a: ampullopetal. b: ampullofugal current; horizontal canal left). In the first part of his film, Steinhausen consecrates a sequence to the functioning of the maritime compass (Traegheits-kompass). This sequence is followed by another which represents a very crude model of the ampula of the semicircular canal; this model is then mounted in three dimensions in order to obtain a schematic representation of the labyrinth. In a series of images one can see the different reactional movements of this rubber cupula to various physical stimulations. It is only then that the completely experimental part of the film begins (and with it the source of errors of interpretation). The series of images, entitled "Kupula etwas geschrumpft," are shown first and seem to confirm the model on all points. This series of images should have been placed at the end of the film, for it is then that the experimenter, in creating an artifical labyrinthic overpressure, succeeds in more or less unsoldering this membrane which we know is ordinarily pressed against the distal wall. In taking Steinhausen's experimental material piece by piece and in analysing it image by image we have been able to find, particularly concerning the labyrinthic rotatory stimulation, a document which is very much the expression of what is happening. Far from being an imaginary construction, we note that the recorded phenomenon responds perfectly to the normal biological distribution by Gauss-Laplace. In fact, of the thirteen various positions that the cupula takes during the experiment, we can consider twelve as metamorphic and one as orthomorphic by reference. The total perrotatory deformation is also represented.

sharp resonator in the air, it becomes loose by immersion: the case of the cupula is different, for, as we have seen, its mechanical characteristics are very close to those of the medium (the endolymph) in which it is immerged. Let us suppose then, that a resonator, deadened or not, begins a forced vibration through the action of a periodical cause (we can once more imagine the alternating vestibulary chair by DeVries, perfected by Hennebert), in changing the phase of this periodical cause, it will become conflicting with the vibration of the resonator and the latter will be cancelled out: the resonator will fall into a state of rest. It will not remain so, as the cause continues to exert its action it will begin to vibrate again in phase with the cause. This fact, experimentally verified in the case of the cupulary resonator, permits the reader to conceive of how, through the action of a movement of endolymphic liquid of the semicircular canals, a movement which has its starting point in the canals themselves, following a voluntary or forced movement of the head, in relation to which we know that the semicircular canals constitute a perfectly subservient system, how then a liquid current striking an elastic membrane can create a system of waves which, considering the inertia of the liquid (cause of latency and reactional excess), registers itself statistically in the temporal and spatial margins of the applied stimulus. We have, in short, to take up what was mentioned above, the following phenomenon: cessation of vibrations and then resumption. This effect is extremely important from the point of view of theory. We know that on the other hand the resonator vibrates in phase with the cause only in resonance. When we deviate, a difference in phase appears which varies continuously in function with the frequency and passes from $-\pi/2$ at one side of the resonance curve to $+\pi/2$ on the other; for frequencies distant from the resonance, the cause and the resonator are in opposition of phase. The variation of phase is more rapid than the variation of amplitude. These are so many experimental facts, notably the very important phenomenon of difference of phase, seen according to criteria most judiciously applied and closest undoubtedly to the deepest sense of the experiments.

We can define the behaviour of the resonator in a regime of forced oscillations by the notion of *passing band*. This is the interval of frequencies where one can consider that the resonator functions well, a definition which is obviously somewhat arbitrary. It is nevertheless the basis for the determination of the *threshold of vestibulary excitability* measured by diverse authors according to diverse initial definitions.

The notion of passing band is useful for studying the case of an electrical amplifier, a construction which receives an alternate current of v frequency by two entry terminals. The difference of potential at the entry terminals is:

$$\triangle V_E = x_E \cos 2\pi v E \quad (3.2.63)$$

At the exit of the apparatus we pick up, in permanent regime, a difference of alternate potential of the same frequency:

$$\triangle V = x \cos 2\pi v E \quad (3.2.64)$$

The amplification of the tension is x/x_E and it is arranged that it will be superior to the unity (we often use the notation in decibels for amplification. Its value is then: $20 \log x/x_E$). In fact, such an apparatus is nothing other than a resonator of period property T_o and of frequency property v_o. When the frequency v of the current is equal to the frequency of the resonance, the tension at the exit is x_o. We can, naturally, describe the phenomena as we have heretofore: there is for the amplifier a constant of time $\tau = 1/B$ that we make equal to $T_o/2\pi\varepsilon$. ε is a number proportional to the coefficient of deadening since $B = 2\pi\varepsilon/T_o$. This number can vary for diverse regulations of the apparatus when it is equal to 1, it defines the *critical deadening;* the resonator is then so deadened that its own frequency no longer appears in the transitory regime. When it is different from 1, ε is the relationship of the coefficient of actual deadening with the coefficient of critical deadening; it is usually always inferior to 1. It is necessary to note, in fact, that the regime of critical deadening is of no practical interest, for the oscillations of regime take a long time to appear. The calculation shows that we have:

for the logarithmic decrement: $\delta = 2\pi\varepsilon$

for the acuteness of the resonance: $\pm\varepsilon$.

The value of the amplification of the resonance is then:

$$x_o/x_E = \tfrac{1}{2}\,\varepsilon \quad (3.2.65)$$

As it is desired in practice that it have a high value, we are led to
diminish ε, that is to work far from the critical regime, in high
resonance. In a general way:

$$x = \frac{v_o^2 x_E}{\sqrt{(v_o^2-v^2)^2+4\varepsilon^2 v_o^2 v^2}} \qquad (3.2.66)$$

In loose resonance, that is when we want the apparatus to respond to many frequencies, the amplification diminishes much
and even for values of ε closest to 1 we have an attenuation. (The
values of ε for us in this case are comprised, indicatively, between
0,5 and 0,7.) The passing band is the interval of frequency where
the amplification remains great; we thus adopt, as a convention
for great, an amplification equal to half of that obtained for the
resonance. If we look for the value of the amplification in the field
of frequencies which define the acuteness of the resonance (a
field contained in the passing band since it is delimited by $v_o(1\pm\varepsilon)$,

we find: $x/x_E = \dfrac{1}{\sqrt{2}} x_o/x_E \qquad (3.2.67)$

This great conventional amplification is defined by the values of
the frequencies:

$$v_1 = v_o (1\text{-}\varepsilon \sqrt{3}) \text{ and } v_2 = v_o (1 + \varepsilon \sqrt{3}) \qquad (3.2.68)$$

Its width is thus:

$$2v_o \varepsilon \sqrt{3} \qquad (3.2.69)$$

In virtue of the adopted definitions, it is equivalent to say that
a resonator is in harmony; or that its resonance is shrill; or that its
passing band is narrow and that on the other hand its resonance
is loose or blurred; or that its passing band is wide. But it is necessary to draw attention to the fact that the number which measures the acuteness of the resonance is related in form of a bell to
the resonance curve and the more the resonance is shrill the
smaller is the number which measures the acuteness. There is
in effect a sort of play on words for the meaning of the term
acuteness. One should not be astonished to read that resonator
1 possesses a resonance much shriller than resonator 2 and then
that the acuteness (in the qualitative sense) of 1 is inferior to
that of 2. This variation of the qualitative and quantitative sense

of the word acuteness is quite disturbing. Remember finally that
we use in electronics filters which are amplifiers with very narrow
passing bands (pass-band filters), certain of which letting past
only frequencies superior to a certain frequency called the cutting
off frequency (high-pass filters). There exist low-pass filters also.
Considering the mechanical analogy of these filters in the bound-
ed system of rotatory vestibular stimulator and vestibular sensorial receptor, we notice that one of the essential conditions of
the continuous stimulator (non-alternating like the DeVries

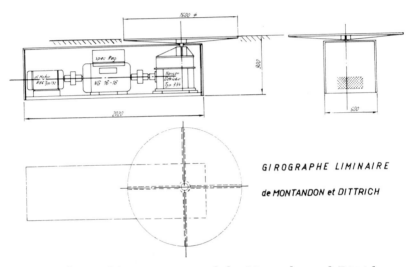

GIROGRAPHE LIMINAIRE

de MONTANDON et DITTRICH

FIG. 30. Schema of liminary gyrograph by Montandon and Dittrich, precision vestibulatory stimulator for clinical usage. The plate supporting the
chair is pulled by an electrohydraulic system of propulsion, i.e., pump with
variable debit HT of Von Roll, permitting an angular acceleration rigorously
constant for a spector of values comprised between 0,2-20⁰/sec². The hy-
draulic variator is pulled by an electric servomotor which progressively
regulates the flux furnished by the pump: this is fed by another motor
developing 4 HP. All the units of this system are related to a mechanical
reducer placed directly under the plate. The different elements of the pro-
pulsor group—placed in a completely soundproof common case—are related
among each other by periflex joints permitting the suppression of all mechanical vibrations. The subject examined is thus placed in optimal conditions of silence, the posterior labyrinth only being stimulated, without
cochlear vibratory afferences; the visual afferences are suppressed by placing the apparatus in a darkened room.

chair) is the *constancy of its angular acceleration,* which in vestibulometry plays the role of pass band filter. The only stimulator responding entirely to this exigency is the "Liminary Gyrograph" by Montandon and Dittrich (see Fig. 30) in which one
can see the "passband effect" on the nystagmic vestibulary reaction consecutive to a stimulus of the same absolute value but
in which the intensity-acceleration repartition is not common
(Fig. 31).

Without going into the detail of the diverse resonators (tune
forks, Helmholtz resonators, etc.), we would like to recall briefly
some basic elements related to vibrating cords. Take a cord of
length L stretched between two points. T is its tension, m its
mass by unity of length; its fundamental frequency is:

$$v_0 = \tfrac{1}{2} L \sqrt{T/m} \quad (3.2.70)$$

We see thus that the fundamental frequency is:

    a) inversely proportional to its length,

    b) proportional to the square root of its tension,

    c) inversely proportional to the square root of m.

These laws are not valid for symmetrical resonators, that is to
say freely vibrating resonators. The cupular resonator—the experiments of Ewald have shown—is a case of a *dissymmetrical
resonator,* or a resonator for which displacement in one direction
is hampered; in fact, according to the direction of the stimulation one of the sides of the membrane is more loaded than the
other. We know that a symmetrical resonator submitted to two
simultaneous sounds of frequencies v_1 and v_2, will take a movement which will be the sum of the two and where frequencies v_1
and v_2 will thus appear. The theory of dissymmetrical resonators
shows that in their case what appears besides is frequency $2v_1$
and $2v_2$ (2nd order of harmonics), $v_1 + v_2$ (its additive) and $v_1 - v_2$
(its differential) as well as numerous accessory vibrations such as
$2v_1 \pm v_2$, $2v_2 \pm v_1$, $3v_1 \pm v_2$, etc.

Before terminating these biophysical considerations on the intimacy of the cupulary functioning, we would like to mention
rapidly a few generalizations relating to the oscillations of relaxation which will be abundantly introduced in our fourth section. We consider, in classical acoustics only sinusoidal oscilla-

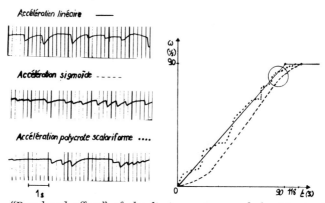

ᴇꜰꜰᴇᴛs sur **l** *NYSTAGMUS d'ACCELERATIONS ANGULAIRES de* 1/s²

(GAH - même sujet normal - même étalonnage)

Accélération linéaire   ———

Accélération sigmoïde - - - - -

Accélération polycrote scalariforme ....

1s

FIG. 31. "Pass-band effect" of the liminary gyrograph by Montandon and Dittrich. The first tracing (linear acceleration according to the rotatory liminary test by Montandon) is a normal tracing characteristic of the nystagmic vestibulary reaction of which the amplitude is regular and so is the frequency; the latter is situated, for the accelometric liminary value at 1⁰/sec²., at a value of about 1 Hz. The second tracing (sigmoid acceleration) shows a net diminishing of the amplitude and a concomitant augmentation of the frequency which can lead one to think either of a pathological tracing or possibly of a normal tracing consecutive with a much more intense stimulation that we are seeking (from which comes the pass-band effect of the stimulator, permitting the preceding recording). The phenomenon recorded during the second tracing is due to the characteristics of the stimulators "electronically" driven and corrected for which the latency time modifies quite a bit the value of the efficient stimulation slope; one can easily realize this phenomenon by comparing the continuous and discontinuous curves on the diagram, or even better in trying to inscribe the discontinuous curve in an interval of 90 sec. and not 118 sec., the latter interval being chosen for the adjustment of efficient stimulation slopes. The last tracing of this figure (scalariform polycrote acceleration) has only a purely comparative interest.

tions. We have seen how, in the second section of this work, we have been able to approach these phenomena in a less classical but decidedly more physical manner. We have also followed the development of this third section where it was primarily necessary to introduce the more generalized notion of acoustics.

Now it is easier to understand that the sinusoidal oscillations, otherwise than they have always previously been known, have met with such great favour in acoustics since their mathematical manipulation is one of the simplest: the theorem by Fourier introduces them in any periodical phenomenon and it seems that series of sinus, Fourierian or not, suit the hearing mechanism. Even so, electronic progress has shown that the case of sinusoidal oscillations was much too simplistic and that, in certain circumstances, and without much difficulty, an oscillator could take several regimes of oscillation. In any case, the permanent regime is preceded by a transitory regime. There exists, besides, a whole series of intermediaries between the classical oscillatory regime and a crude regime called *relaxation;* we point out that the latter regime is essentially asymmetrical, diphasic, containing, contrary to the sinusoidal regime, a slow component and a long component of elongation in function of time.

We must realize well the idea that the periodicity of pure sounds introduces of itself a decomposition in series of sinus or cosinus as a mathematical artifice of study. The experimental decomposition confers on it a physical reality. As we have already remarked, the sinus series, from a mathematical point of view, are quite handy and permit the obtaining of solutions of many differential equations of current type. We could say that this is the reason for their good fortune in electricity. But we also see that electrical vibratory systems were regulated by differential equations which do not admit of a sinus solution. It is a frequent case in electronics. Equations for which the solution is sinusoidal often rest, concerning the study of vibrations, on large approximations and assume a schematic almost qualitative aspect. Many equations relative to the vibrating systems admit as a solution very different functions than sinus, but having common mathematical characteristics with them. It is easier, in this case, for the study of a phenomenon, even if it is periodic, to represent it by an unlimited series of these functions, in the manner of a series by Fourier. The mathematical artifice is of identical nature and has no other weight or physical signification. In particular, it does not imply, unless one demonstrates it to the contrary, that the decomposed signal is physically composed of preexistent elementary signals representable by the type of function chosen for the development.

The type of function which serves the mathematical development is imposed by the behaviour of the receptor and not by the signal. We use, needless to say, currently in electronics the decomposition in series of functions by Bessel, Mathieu, in polynomes by Tschebycheff, Legendre, Laguerre, etc...... even when the signal is periodic. Since the vibratory dynamic of the ear does not admit of the sinusoidal solution, it is thus not out of the question, a priori, that the response to a complex excitation be, mathematically, studiable by a decomposition in non-Fourierian series. Actually, the Fourier series has no privilege outside of the case of pure sounds where one is obliged to study the behaviour of an isolated sinusoidal function. It is suitable to note that outside of a physical group of pure sounds (musical sounds), the series of sinus is physically imposed for the entry signal, but it is clear that other decompositions are mathematically possible. For non-periodic vibrations, on the other hand, the problem is quite different. The essential part of the orientative function is a coding and decoding, this is valid for the auditive function also and experience is mute on the necessity of passing through a series of sinus. The difference which separates the electrical and acoustical mathematical conceptions of a signal appear clearly when one studies a modulated alternative signal. Let us consider the sinusoidal signal described by the law:

$$x = a \cos (2\pi vE + \varphi) \qquad (3.2.71)$$

it is defined by its amplitude a, its frequency v and its phase φ in relation to a signal of reference. Normally these three quantities remain constant: the signal is called modulated when one of these quantities, or the three, vary in time in a periodical fashion. In electronics, the term modulation is used in a more restrained sense: the variable quantity has a periodical variation which is very weak around a relatively fixed value, the frequency of this variation v' is itself, most often, quite inferior to the frequency of the signal which we call carrying wave. It follows that the variable quantity never cancels itself out. We limit ourselves to this case. Let us consider the most simple modulation, where only the amplitude of the signal is modulated (modulation in amplitude). The signal is described by the law:

$$x = (a + b \cos 2\pi v'E) \cos 2\pi vE \quad (3.2.72)$$

The amplitude a of the carrying frequency v is modulated by $b \cos 2\pi v'E$, b is very inferior to a. We call the quantity b/a the degree of modulation. We can transform a perfectly legitimate transformation for the mathematician, the expression of the law (72) and obtain law (74), strictly equivalent:

$$x = a \cos 2\pi vE + b \cos 2\pi v'E \cdot \cos 2\pi vE \quad (3.2.73)$$

from which

$$b_x = b/2 \cos 2\pi \, (v + v')E + a \cos 2\pi v \, E + b/2 \cos 2\pi \, (v - v')E \quad (3.2.74)$$

The physicist might be tempted to say that we have caused the existence of three formants of which it is the sum to appear in the signal: the first of frequency $v + v'$, the second of frequency v (the most important) and the third of frequency $v - v'$. *If the signal (72) is an electrical signal*, the reasoning is completely accurate: (72) can be furnished by an alternator, of which the internal resistance varies periodically and the signal will be its electromotor force, one can treat the modulated current as a sum of currents following the law (74) and in particular if one wants the amplifier, make the signal pass in a battery of three filters, of the same relation of amplification and of which the passing-bands are centered on $v + v'$, $v - v'$ and v; the three currents are mixed again at the exit of the filters and the resulting current follows the law (72) except in the amplification. On the contrary, *if the signal (72) is an acoustical signal* that is to say a material vibration, the decomposition according to law (74) is physically false. In fact, the study of sound with the aid of a battery of resonators consisting of systems capable of responding to the three frequencies $v+v'$, $v-v'$ and v, the only one will be the resonator harmonized with v, the others remaining silent. The vibrations $v + v'$ and $v - v'$ are thus not elementary sounds forming the complex sound (72): the equivalence of laws (72) and (74) is purely analytical. The vibration of resonator will undergo variations of intensity which translate the modulation in amplitude of the unique sound. The sound (72) can be produced in many manners, as, for example, by a resonator whose exciting cause varies periodically in amplitude. This case holds an interesting lesson: one can wish to amplify, near the source or far away, a modulated sound (T.S.F.; T.V.). For this, we pick up the sound on a microphone which transforms it into modulated current like the incidental sound, that is to say, following law (72). By application of what was said above, we can amplify this current by passage in a battery of filters, that is by using for it the decomposition foreseen by law (74) *acoustically false*. The amplified current acts on a loud speaker acoustical resonator electrically excited by a current of variable amplitude: it emits a sound with identical frequency to that of the primitive sound modulated in intensity according to law (72) and amplified in relation to its incident. We can thus study in the same way a signal modulated in frequency following the law:

$$x = a \cos (2\pi v E + b/v' \sin 2\pi v' E) \quad (3.2.75)$$

equivalent if b/v' is small to the law:

$$x = \frac{ab}{2\pi v'} \cos 2\pi (v+v') E + a \cos 2\pi v E - \frac{ab}{2\pi v'} \cos 2\pi (v-v')E \quad (3.2.76)$$

We see, thus, that we can pass from an acoustical signal to another by means of an acoustical decomposition without signification. From their first pages, works on acoustics insist on the nature of the relations existing between these various laws to warn physicists. We have thought it well to insist on it once more to forewarn our physiologist readers against the hasty attribution of a precise physical signification or of a definite physiological sense for a frequency found during harmonic analysis of the electrical translation of a physiological signal: this individualization of frequencies, possible if the signal is of an electrical nature (electronystagmogram) must be controlled very closely if the original signal is of a mechanical nature (cupulogram). The systematic recourse to the development by Fourier is not justified in physiology; only the natural physical development possesses a value. And then its validity ends when the initial phenomenon undergoes a translation which changes its nature.

The reader has thus been able to familiarize himself, after anatomy and physiology, with the biophysical dissection of the cupular mechanism, key mechanism of the sense of orientation. He has followed the various stages of this process which have led him from the nature of the vestibulary stimulus (a generator of molecular vibrations) to the transfer of this signal along a line (which we have called the compromise "interface-plate"), the reception of this signal by the dissymmetrical cupular resonator which functions also as transducer of energy.*

We have thus attained the limit of that which the physicist has the right to examine. But before conceding our place to the cybernetics which will attempt to integrate these processes in a general regulator mechanism of the sense of orientation, with its various afferences, we must clear up certain concepts which are still blurred, even point up certain erroneous conceptions relative to the vestibule, a precaution without which the reader risks to fall prey to certain prejudices which will harm his judgment.

Note: The theory of the ballistic galvanometer is also better adapted than that of the torsion pendulum because the ballistic galvanometer is only dependent on one parameter—time; all depend on the stimulation which can be greater or smaller than the characteristic time.

EQUILIBRIUM AND EQUILIBRATION

THE LABYRINTH IS often defined as the organ of equilibrium; as such it is classed among the sense organs in many books on physiology. For certain authors—we borrow this commentary from Ledoux—the function of equilibrium is so integrated in the complex of motor reactions of the central nervous system that its study would best be found in a chapter dealing with all the postural reflexes. From the physiological point of view, in fact, equilibrium cannot be considered as a state of rest, since it concerns a living body of which all the parts are gifted with activity. We know that in a particular position which may appear as a perfect state of equilibrium, the body actually undergoes continual oscillations. Retaining this position is only possible, in a living being composed of articulated segments, if multiple muscular contractions hold the center of gravity of the body above its plane of sustenance. In the same way, equilibrium during a movement will be obtained by the perfect harmonization of the muscular work regulating the displacement in function of energy, time and space and always assuring, between two determined attitudes, a perfect equivalence of the forces in presence.

As we have already emphasized, three principal factors intervene in the regulation of equilibrium: superficial and profound sensitivity, vision, and the labyrinth. These factors have a relative importance variable in the various animal species according to way of life and environment. Fish move in an environment where profound sensitivity and vision cannot play an important role. The labyrinth is there developed to a considerable extent and its destruction brings on serious difficulties in orientation. The amphibians, living on both land and water, also present important problems in orientation when the labyrinth is destroyed; these troubles are however compensated for in amphibians to the extent that they can profit from their sensitivity to contact in the plane of sustenance. In the same way, birds without labyrinth are capable of moving on the ground but cannot fly nor direct themselves. In man, on the other hand, as in other mammals, the labyrinth has lost a part of its importance of profound sensitivity and vision. The following examples will help in understanding the profound reality which places the sense of *orientation* and not the sense of equilibrium in the vestibule:

The deaf-mute, whose labyrinths are non-functioning, enjoys perfect equilibrium. If he is blind, his stability is still greatly assured by his profound sensations. On the other hand, the tabetic whose eyes and labyrinths are intact has only a precarious equilibrium. This equilibrium becomes impossible if he is blind or deaf-mute.

The cerebral hemispheres, the cerebellum and the labyrinth are not necessary for this reaction—only the contact of the soles with a resistant plane suffices to provoke, by the play of the myotatic reflex, a group of muscular reactions at the level of all segments of the body, permitting the upright position and the maintenance of a *fundamental equilibrium*.

In the same way, any change of position of the head in relation to the body starts off reactions of equilibration having their origin in the profound sensitivity of the muscles and articulations of the neck. On all this complex mechanisms of fundamental equilibrium which has its origin in the profound sensitivity, there come into action with more or less efficiency, according to the degree of animal evolution, vestibulary and visual functions. The constitution of a single and stereoscopic field of vision has given to vision such importance that it has pushed the vestibulary function into a very secondary role, at least apparently; we know, and we will have the occasion to come back to it further along, that the vestibule is, as it were, the coordinating center of all the information, also the regulating center of position, which makes it, along with the other sensorial apparatuses, the seat of the sense of orientation. It is convenient here to come to agreement on a play on words which may seem disagreeable to the physiologist: when we speak of "center" we only refer with this word to a very general sense of it as "the central point of a system of information" and not in the generally accepted sense of the term to designate the nervous centers. In fact, the role of the vestibulary apparatus is to inform the nervous centers on the position of the head at each instant and on all the movements, particularly angular ones, that it executes in relation to a tricoordonometric system of reference. The vestibule participates in the setting off of reactions having as result the maintenance—or in other words, the orientation—of the head in normal position and the conservation of the permanence of the initial visual field, an important condition of the orientative system. It comes into play in the whole ensemble of muscular reactions of orientation of the trunk and the extremities. The vestibule represents, microcosmically, the tricoordonometric system of the subject in motion in relation to a fixed tricoordonometric system of reference, exterior to the subject in motion. The cinematic relativist conditions the relations of these two systems to one another.

STIMULATION AND TRANSDUCTION

We HAVE SEEN THAT the gelatine of the cupula envelopes the cilia of the sensorial cells. The base of the cupula has one of its insertions fixed on the ampullary crista, the other pressing against the vault of the ampulla. Some authors still believe that the summit of the cupulary insertion is not pressed but leaves a narrow capillary split and that, afterwards, because of the total close of the endolymphatic space by the cupula, this is mechanically coupled with the endolymph; it followed that each endolymphatic current must lead to an inclination of the cupula. We have shown before what the physical conditions were of the bounding of the cupula-endolymphatic system, notably by the necessity of an adaptor of impedances system, corollary to the experimentation. There are to be found, however, among physiologists and some physicists, ardent defenders of the deviational cupulary movement pre- and post-stimulatory. Thus the measurement of the duration of the oscillation of the cupula-endolymph system has been attributed to Steinhausen. This duration, evaluated at 20 seconds, has been the object of numerous controversies and of an equation. The equation of deadened forced oscillation, that is to say the lineal differential equation of the second order proposed by Groen describes completely the functional conduct of the cupula-endolymph system. We have taken the liberty of presenting objections at several points to this equation, basis of the hypothesis called "pendulum of cupulary torsion"; such an approximation, gross and improbable as it is, is nonetheless attractive and ends by being, like the Cartesian "discourse of method," not an instrument of work, a means for reaching further knowledge, but an end in itself, a goal, a law. This is the reason for which we have insisted on leaving the succinct exposition of it to the end of this chapter. In order not to modify the thought of the authors of this delicate work, we have judged it simplest to give, *in extenso,* one of the significant texts which have appeared on this subject: "on the effect of continuous acceleration" (Ek, Jongkees and Klijn):

> "... In a series of experiments, van Egmond, Groen and Jong-
> kees have given a mechanical analysis of the phenomena in
> response to the stimulation of the semicircular canals. They
> stated that the system of the endolymph-cupula is a pendu-
> lum system, sensitive to angular acceleration and following
> the mechanical laws. Many objections against this mechanical
> way of considering the function of the vestibular organ are
> brought forward and it must be admitted that man as such is
> no exact mechanical instrument. Van Egmond, Groen and
> Jongkees eventually were able, on the basis of a number of
> experiments, to measure the constants of the equation for the
> cupula-endolymph system in the human being.

"The differential equation of a torsion pendulum, where there are no external forces, is

$$\theta \, \ddot{\xi} + \pi \, \dot{\xi} + {}^\triangle \xi = 0$$

directly upon the deviation of the cupula.

θ = moment of inertia of the cupula,

π = moment of friction at unit angular velocity,

$\triangle$ = directional momentum at unit angle,

ξ = angular deviation of the endolymph relative to the skull,

$\dot{\xi}$ = angular velocity of the endolymph relative to the skull,

$\ddot{\xi}$ = angular acceleration of the endolymph relative to the skull.

According to the theory of Van Egmond, Groen and Jongkees, there is no sensation of rotation as long as the cupula is in its zero position (at least as long as it is not deviated from the mid-position over a greater angle than is necessary to reach the threshold), and a deviated cupula causes a certain sensation of rotation; the same deviation gives rise to the same sensation. The deviation of the cupula is a measure of the subjective speed of rotation. The sensation is *supposed* to depend upon it. With the aid of a great number of experiments Van Egmond *et al.*, found the value of the coefficients. $\pi/\triangle$ can be measured in cupulometry, $\triangle/\theta$ is calculable from resonance vibrations on a torsion swing. In this way the differential equation becomes

$$\ddot{\xi} + 10 \, \dot{\xi} + \xi = 0$$

It seemed that in normal subjects the sensation was completely proportional to the deviation of the cupula. In many instances quantitative data found in rotatory tests coincided beautifully with the predictions given by the equation. Cupulometry, therefore, does not only have its clinical value; it gives a strong support to the theoretical basis. It would seem that the cerebrum is functioning as a perfect registration apparatus of the cupula. . . ."

We have previously made the case for several objections. We will now make those that we have already published on this subject: they are two in number. The first in that it is as yet impossible to measure *in a directly reproducible manner* in man the three constants and the three factors above. This objection alone would suffice to definitely remove from the world the ingenious constructions of such a differential equation. The second objection is furnished by the fact that the most classic data as well as the most recent data of sensorial histo-physiology concord in bringing forward non-linear phenomena and even better, non-linearly deadened in time; one of the most peremptory arguments resides in the fact that anisotrophy of the cupula confers on it differential mechanical properties according to the directions.

We lack thus only a concept, founded on experiment, of the transformation of the mechanical stimulus into excitation of the sensorial cells of the ampullary crista. The merit of Trinker's work is to have given us this concept:

". . . The inclination of the cilla is the adequate stimulus for all the sensorial cells of the labyrinthic organs. The inclination in one direction causes a depolarization of the cellular membrane; in the opposite direction, a hyperpolarization. The characteristic curve of these variations of potential results in the form of an S, like the characteristic curve of the frequency of potentials of action, derived from isolated fibers of the ampullary nerve. The continuous resting potential is maintained by the cellular metabolism. The extension of lipo-proteic structures of the membrane produces the mentioned variations of potential, which function as "potential generators": they excite or inhibit the discharging mechanism in form of nervous influx, increasing or diminishing its frequency."

The very recent works by Green, Rauch and others on mito-chondries have permitted the precise statement of the intimate nature of this mechanism of energetic transduction (Energie-Umwandlungsart) until then devolving upon the most diverse agents.

To summarize, the labyrinthic receptor of the semicircular canals cannot be considered as a prolongation-transducer (selon opinion of many authors) but as a transformer of tension in angu-lar displacement units.

SECTION FOUR

ELEMENTS OF COCHLEO-VESTIBULAR CYBERNETICS

INTRODUCTION

"In restraining its object in a decisive manner, science can come to know it better since it is made to measure. But schemas of intelligibility which take into account this abstract object are obviously simplistic and simplified and cannot have a value beyond their limited jurisdiction. The technician who has constructed a motor or an electronic machine can flatter himself that he knows the anatomy and the physiology of these apparatuses in a more or less complete manner. But it would be a thoughtless attempt on his part should he pretend to compare the functioning of an organism with that of his machine. Knowledge of a small-scale model is only authoritative for the small-scale model; outside its particular field it can without doubt offer elements suggestive to comprehension, but it is never a question of anything but topics and ideas and comparison is not reason. The man who takes the vow of science becomes unfaithful to that vow when, leaving the framework which he fixed for himself, he gives himself, at the price of confusion of genus, an authority he does not possess."

(G. Gusdorf)

In the words of Moles, cybernetics is a "cross-roads science." Its platonic name covers a precise field of mental operations which is in contact with multiple sciences and technics: all those which concern themselves with *organisms*. In fact, cybernetics is itself a branch of a larger science, automation. It is known that the basis of automation is on the one hand mechanical, thermic and electrical machines, on the other hand metrological technics, electronics, automatic numerical calculation, mathematics and logic, the technics of telecommunications and the theory of information. Automation has become an independent science and a new technic with notions, definitions, methods, new criteria and a specific instrumentation. It can be said at the present time that the principal field of activity of automation includes seven principal groups:

137

—automatic measurement

—automatic command

—automatic regulation

—automatic calculation

—automatic superior operations

—automatic treatment of information and language

—Cybernetics, the study of automatic procedures in living beings.

One of the characteristics of the scientific spirit of this century has been to develop a science which was descriptive and classificatory into a *science of models*. For each natural phenomenon, we seek today to make a corresponding model, that is to say an organism which functions in the same manner as the original phenomenon, but at the scale of the observer. And this is true even when the microscopic constitution of the observed structure differs greatly from the model which represents it. Cybernetics has posed, for example, the question: "What is a cochlea?" as a work axiom, and, on the basis of its statistically verified functioning, of its reactions in diverse experimental conditions, cybernetics has been able to create a model reproducing this comportment in its details and its incertitudes. The highest scientific distinction, the Nobel Prize, rewards the work of he who by his experiments answers such a seemingly simple question. This alone is proof that cybernetics is not an elementary discipline.

Actually, cybernetics rests on the operation concept of the quadripole, an element to which we alluded previously in introducing the theory of lines. In its simplest representation, the quadripole is a physical structure, made up of an entrance, an exit, and a specific function for each given structure, expressing the variations of the size of the exit in terms of the size of the entrance. An example, among others, of the quadripole is the electronic *filter* in which one applies a signal having a certain form to the entrance, the same signal having another different form at the exit. The concept of the quadripole is susceptible to a quasi-indefinite generalization: a relay is a quadripole in which the size of the entrance is the current of excitation, and the size of the exit the disposition of the electrical circuit to which the contact of the relay belongs; a computing machine is a quadripole at the entrance of which one puts certain mathematical figures and which furnishes at the exit another series of figures starting with a certain *transformation* function, to which the name *program* has been given.

Cybernetics has as its object the study of reactions to message and the interactions of complex systems of quadripoles in terms of their internal structure. In a great majority of cybernetic problems, the organisms to be studied must be considered as transformers of information. In machines of control and regulation the name *decision* is given to the particular structure taken into the interior of a particular quadripole with the action of a message; in the same way, the name *action* is given to the phenomenon which manifests itself externally as the size of the exit. Cybernetics can also be distinguished from the science of communications by the use it makes of *chains of quadripoles with closed loops*. In this kind of set up, some form of feedback is exercised by the output signal on the input signal, creating a connecting of the message to a goal, final term, which has here an objective sense: it is the deviation between the actual size and the discounted size which conditions at each instant the action of the machine to correct that deviation, thus creating autonomous systems which directly utilize the energy furnished them to accomplish a final result inscribed in the structure of the system.

The regulation practiced in the electrical centers takes into consideration a system of data and finds an adequate solution for it. Spinoza claimed that the intelligence was the carrying out of an adequate step in unforeseen circumstances in terms of a scale of values; one can detect in the regulators of an electrical center the embryo of a specialized "intelligence" achieving the homeostasy of a system. Beyond the stage of regulation, the servo-mechanisms attach to the action a countersign value furnished by a model, a perforated card for example. The stage of *programming* itself is already at a higher level of complexity: the machine manipulates the data (analogic or digital computers, detecting units). Further on we describe the structure and the functioning of a machine which marks an important stage in auditive cybernetics: the Phonetograph by J. Dreyfus-Graf.

The analogy between these remarkable creations and the human brain has not escaped the cyberneticians: mechanical thought does not differ from the elementary stage of human thought; the mode of cerebral functioning however would appear to be radically different from that of the big analogical machines and this despite the use in both cases of a binary codification. The brain furnishes, as a matter of fact—and here is one essential difference —correct results, independent of errors for each of its constituant cells. We know that this aptitude is so strong that a massive destruction involving about half of the constituant cells does not notably affect the quality and quantity of thought. This difference is not, however, *fundamental;* it is a difference of degree and not of nature: it is principally due, as Moles points out, to the fact that thought is a message whose structure is determined in a *statistical* fashion, and not an *exact* fashion.

It is evident that cybernetics of superior functions is far from satisfactory solutions. These solutions will only come into being progressively on the basis of elements of information and of solutions reached in the different sensorial and vegetative functions. It is, in fact, from the interaction of these diverse functions that voluntary motoricity results, in large part.

One would ask at this point what utility, other than speculative, is attached to cybernetics. To this question we respond that cybernetics is, in a certain sense, the art of assuring the efficacity of action. This term efficacity permits at the same time the distinction between cybernetics and ordinary sciences which attempt to bring received information into the framework of thought given *a priori* in order to describe the world and its behaviour; cybernetics attempts to bring this information into forms adapted to circumstances in order to act upon the world with efficacity.

Experience shows that the world is not one of infinite diversity, that nature repeats itself everywhere more or less rigorously. In studying any complex system, it happens frequently that one discovers that certain properties are easier to manipulate than others; the schema includes easy regions and other difficult ones. It is for cybernetics to find another schema which corresponds to the first and which it can use as a sort of plan. The difficult problems presented by the first schema can then be easily resolved by examining the corresponding part of the second: this is the definition of the model. One can see the importance of the role played by mathematics in science: it serves in the making of schemas. The example of mathematical physics is pertinent in this sense: it is a science which uses mathematics to move with certitude among real objects. The most precise example, to come back to it again, that of the pendulum, is demonstrative: a mathematical physicist knows from the start how to pass from the material mass to a universe of harmonic functions and differential equations. He can thus pass without delay from the problem to the solution, in so far as the premises of his syllogism have been correctly posed. As a last step he has just to retranslate the obtained expression into expressions of the material universe. Then what is essential in this method of plans appears clearly: one finds oneself in the presence of two schemas, one which is traced by the actual pendulum as it moves effectively, and the other developed by the functions of the mathematical universe. Laws exist according to which one can relate certain elements of the first schema to certain elements of the second. One notices too that this method of conversion of schemas is more rapid, experimentally, than the operation directly executed on the material world which is then no more than a stage of verification, of control of a schematic hypothesis of chosen work. Isomorphic schemas are spoken of in such cases and it has been seen repeatedly that the study of a real system can be facilitated by the study of a system which is isomorphic to it. An analogy is only a feeble form of isomorphism where the schema is not rigorously determined nor is the resemblance exact. Thus every physical system of which the activity is well defined will generate well-defined schemas of comportment; several systems can, of course, generate the same schema and in this case one may consider one of the systems as essential and the others as accessory plans. One can thus say, as we did above, that one of these plans constitute the *model* of the principal system.

Schemas having been worked out, one can then verify if they are definite, reproducible, useful. We might add that to be useful they must, in a certain field of validity, be isomorphic to another system of primordial interest of which the technical control remains difficult. Only mathematical models, with rare exception, satisfy these conditions. Mechanical models are only in their beginnings and one can imagine that one of the major preoccupations of science in the century to come will be the making of models.

It would be erroneous however to bind oneself without reserves to the verity of a model. As perfectly as a plan, a model, a mathematical theory accords with the actual facts and as great be their field of application, yet one should always be prepared to find that after having sufficiently progressed they are no longer suitable. This removes nothing from the merits and the qualities of all the possible models or analogies which must be used to all useful ends. It is fitting however never to lose sight of the fact that a model can be exhausted from one day to another to represent the real and that then it must be modified or replaced.

Much as mathematics has long provided for the working out of isomorphic schemas, it shows itself progressively incapable of resolving by itself the frightening complexity of the ever-growing data of each scientific discipline. The method of models appears then as a sort of last hope. A well-made machine is unquestionably a prolongation of mathematics, on the condition that it is submitted to a rigorous preparation which makes it capable of furnishing reproducible schemas. The computers which we mentioned are only models susceptible of use in scientific fields. The growing complexity in these fields makes verbal expression imprecise and mathematical expression too simple. Only the model can be at the same time precise enough and complex enough. It is easy to predict that if mathematical physics has taken over from physics, mathematics will also move progressively into all the supplementary and connected scientific disciplines: physiology, general biology, psychology and sociology. Once they have been rendered sufficiently isomorphic, that is to say sufficiently close to the actual, these mechanisms will demonstrate what the method of models is capable. Lastly, it is necessary for us to have an awareness of this fundamental postulate which defines the limits of cybernetics:

"There is no difference in the functioning of living beings and mechanical systems."

It is evident that such a definition must be taken "*cum grano salis*," that one must not, in the example of certain scholars, confuse genus and categories. This postulate is the consequence of notions which we have tried to establish previously and applies to the conception of the schema which is perfectly isomorphic.

As we now come nearer to cybernetics of sensorial receptors, we will first say that in general they must be represented by an entity which consists of two distinct parts. The first can be the translator of the message received in a code adapted to the local needs; then the second is the reactor, transforming into acts these messages, starting from certain principles of construction which vary according to the function considered.

In human organisms, the sense organs are virtually systems of codification which transform the apparent continuity of the universe surrounding them into manipulable messages of impulses, according to the principle which digital computers use. Thus the eye can be represented by a mosaic of photoelectric cells juxtaposed, each group of ten cells being equipped with a telegraphic transmitter which measures the number of photons received and sends by the corresponding nerve a telegram consisting of coded impulses. The functioning of the ear is analogous. The system of filters set out along the auditive receptor gives codified configurations following the movement of the endolymph which are transmitted in the manner of a telex-unit. Thus the sensorial receptors generally work in coded impulses. Their role is restricted to transforming the stimuli of the exterior world into impulses belonging to binary logic, conforming to the structure of the internal environment. The exact form of the "tops" recorded is more interesting to the physiologist, whereas the cybernetician will first rely on the principle of all-or-nothing which is that of binary digital machines.

The general principles which summarize the conduct of living beings applies, for the most part, identically to industrial mechanisms. These latter appear then as specialized systems in their functions, however less complete. These principles have been brought together by Grey-Walter and can be summarized thus:

    1. *Principle of simplicity:* Utilize the minimum of organs possible. Between two solutions, one always adopts

that which uses the device containing the minimum apparatus to reach the precise goal intended (Ockham's Razor Principle). The application of this principle, as we have seen it several times throughout this book, is not always easy, and it is sometimes necessary to develop special methods of analysis to solve it.

2. *Principle of Reactivity:* We can best define it by the concept of *reflex* or even *tropism,* the latter having the advantage of being ambivalent.

3. *Principle of Regulation:* This principle is also defined in the notion of *homeostasy,* dear to Claud Bernard.

4. *Principle of Autonomy:* This principle is, in a certain way, a complement of the preceding and adds the notion of *fixity* of environment, answering for the instructural and functional integrity of the system.

The application of these four principles leads to an almost adequate description of the conduct of very inferior living organisms who obey an *optimum ethics.*

5. *Principle of approximation:* This principle differentiates essentially the conduct of living beings and theoretical beings who, themselves, do not live in an approximate manner but in a rational one. The solution of physiological problems is obtained in a hazardous way whereas that of models is not. It is well known however that aleatory fluctuations remain one of the most arduous problems in rational systems.

6. *Principle of exploration:* The life of animated beings is characterized by a spontaneous exploration of the field which is offered them. This principle is mechanically evoked by the technic of sweeping.

7. *Principle of coherence:* Animated systems have a natural tendency to equilibrate two solicitations of opposite tendencies: mechanical equivalents abound.

8. *Principle of society:* This principle is the capacity of these organisms to recognize as intrinsically different from an object, another similar organism, showing only secondary differences with itself. Mechanical models

of attraction and of repulsion consecutive with a detection within definite limits, are easy to make.

9. *Principle of individuality:* Complementary to the preceding, it only increases its specificity (pass-band effect).

10. *Principles of conscience:* The highest of cybernetic principles according to Grey-Walter; it is characterized by the fact that the conduct of the system vis-a-vis its own image is different from that which it would have vis-a-vis an analogous organism.

These ten principles, though they present an extremely general character, are nevertheless quite summary and describe in a very loose fashion the conduct of quite elementary systems. It is indispensable, however, to give the reader a certain familiarity with them, to allow him to glimpse how numerous the difficulties are which remain to be resolved, how vast is the field to be explored, to attempt a generalized cybernetics. This can only be built upon the base of elements, isolated and then regrouped, of vegetative and sensorial mecano-physiology, as we have already stressed. We borrow from A. A. Moles, that Diderot of the twentieth century, the following lines, which will serve here as a conclusion to this brief introduction:

". . . Cybernetics appeared after that as a new way of thinking. It reached the rank of a major technic of knowledge of the external world, in the same way as science is the logical mode of knowledge and art, the aesthetic mode.

Cybernetics comes to know the world in its constitutive parts in creating, by man's hands, functional models without troubling to remake the real: the degree of perfection of the model in its simulation of phenomena, the rate of exactitude with which one reproduces the observed fact plays as great a role in cybernetics as does the hypothesis in traditional science.

To add to that intellectual synthesis of the real by the rational that science proposes in its libraries and its publications, cybernetics suggests to use the functional analogy as the key to the world around is: it wants to complete the libraries with *galeries of models.* To the Hegelian idea of science "the real is the rational," cybernetic thought would add the pragmatic notion of the *functional*.

Cybernetic models then appeared either as servo-mechanisms— in the etymological sense, or as philosophic machines, devices which take apart, demonstrate, illustrate the affirmations of a philosophy conceived as an ethic or rational thought. They give the latter a concrete and often experimental turn, avoiding the principal vice of which the scientific spirit has always accused philosophy: its absence of taste for experiment.

If the philosophic machines have been, up to now, above all models turning abstract notions into concrete ones: that of desire, for example, it can be foreseen that they will rapidly change their destination and that they will pass from a stage of "demonstration of existence" of a materialistic explanation of conduct to that of direct auxiliary of thought to relay to man's imagination and to prolong his capacity for synthesis.

This is why cybernetics, a new type of thought, no matter how ancient its origins, has attracted the interest of philosophers from the very beginning: one must go back to the upsets caused by the crisis of determinism to find a comparable emotion in rational thought. Cybernetics marks a new dimension in the world, a new current: that of *complexity*, to give it the appearance of order; and already cybernetics gives an objective and rational sense to a whole vocabulary which ten years before seemed irremediably soiled with finalism: intention, will, desire are from now on, in models built by our hands, as rational for us as the vectors and coefficients of influence of mechanics and electricity.

But cybernetics, like every weapon of the spirit, possesses two aspects. Besides the galery of models with which it will compete the tools of thought, cybernetics has unquestionable technical aspects. No faculty of man, it would seem, remains outside the possibilities of machines and the young history of cybernetics is staked out by its conquest of fields which until then were considered forbidden. After the regulators the calculation, after calculation, logical thought, after logical thought, the fabrication of programs of action, the translation of foreign languages, the composition of music, the imagination, artistic thought, nothing seems out of bounds for the machine: it is only a question of time and of means; and if the governing machine is still a refuge for humorists, let us remember here that one only mocks what one fears.

Already, following the well-known theorem by Von Neumann, one glimpses machines which reproduce themselves, as the example of cristals in the mother-solution and living beings in a social middle.

Automation, applied science, will introduce its models into everyday life, putting them in the factory, in the office, in private life. Humanity must learn *symbiosis with machines,* life with robots, at the risk perhaps of a populational upset. To learn the rules of this sociology of machines and of men, will "the amplifier of intelligence" become a reality, or must we fall back on the perspectives of modification of man in his living substance which geneticians promise?"

Without commenting on all this remarkable allegory, let us nevertheless restrict ourselves to pointing out that regardless of what one does or thinks, "progress" is less rapid than one cares to say. The flashy rapidity of discoveries and their prolixity are the best measure of its selection: human nature, thank God, changes but slightly and the symbiosis with machines will take place as naturally and as slowly as our capacity for assimilation will permit. That which is not assimilated is thrown out and no matter what, thought will remain the master of the model. One has only to consider the history of those two common senses, hearing and orientation, to realize how premature are these visions of the future, six thousand years old!

PHONETOGRAPH AND AUDITIVE CYBERNETICS

Taking up, with J. Dreyfus-Graf, author of the *Phonetograph*, the idea that at the root of all progress is information, we can say that information confronts what is possible with what exists. It allows one to choose. As we have already emphasized, cybernetics have demonstrated that the primordial mission of information resides in the measurement of error, in order that this can be corrected.

Human information is based, essentially, on spoken language and committing it to readable memory-written language, of which

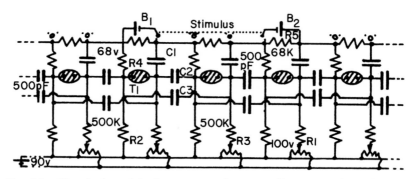

Fig. 32. Electrical model of a nerve. The nerve fiber is a polarized membrane which, receiving at a point of contact certain chemical substances, depolarizes by degrees. The model represented is inspired by the technic of electrical circuits: it consists of a series of sections connected by resistances and condensors which discharge from one section to another. The mechanism of all-or-nothing activity/nonactivity, passivity/nonpassivity is materialized by neon tubes which, as we know have two distinct stable states: lit or unlit. One can regulate the electrical constants to obtain conduction time of about 0.2 m/s. for an element in applying a stimulus at a point. Twenty similar elements represent 5-10 cm of a motor nerve of a frog. After excitation at one point, the system becomes refractory to an ulterior excitation during 0.015 s. Such a model is very close to the physical properties of the biological system.

148

the most powerful kind is alphabetic language. Some thirty very simple graphic signs are sufficient to display or conserve the myriad of thoughts, true or false, which have passed through the minds of men, both past and present. The invention of the alphabet, which was purely phonetic at first, took place circa 1500 B.C., at about the same time as we imagine the Sinai Tablets to have been inscribed.

The automatic transformation of all the sounds of spoken language into alphabetic formulae has, until now, always come up against one of those seemingly insurmountable barriers.

Now then, physics is described as the science of measurable phenomena. In physics a phenomenon does not exist unless there is a receiver capable of measuring it. The ultimate receiver, which is always located in the human brain and senses, is very imprecise by reason of its universality. It needs specialized extensions, such as microscopes, spectrometers, oscillographs, computors and all the mass of other "scopes," "graphs," "meters," and "ators" to discover and come to terms with the laws of nature.

Sounds, in the last instance, are the domain of the auditive receiver, composed of the ear and the brain. Its power of analysis surpasses even the understanding of its owner. But its functioning is not linear and its measurements are often capricious.

Mathematicians, such as Fourier, teach that each sound—however complex it may be—can be considered the sum of an infinity of pure sounds. Unfortunately, pure sounds do not exist in nature any more than infinity does, and as soon as it is a question of sequences of complex sounds, such as in spoken language, mathematicians are incapable of telling us where a sound begins and where it finishes, or what choice must be made in the imbroglio of theoretical components. This is why we are obliged to invent specialised measuring receivers that more precisely imitate certain characteristics of the human receiver, in order to advance the general identification of sounds and their composition.

To begin with, let us summarize the faculties of the auditive receiver (Fig. 33).

The range of frequencies perceived extends over ten octaves, from the 16 c.p.s. of the lowest organ note, to the 16,000 c.p.s. of the shrillest whistle. The piano is limited to seven and a half

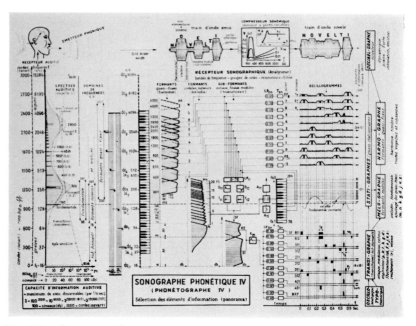

FIG. 33. Phonetograph, prototype IV: selection of elements of information.
(According to J. Dreyfus-Graf.)

octaves, from 27 to 4096 c.p.s. The vibratory amplitude associated
with these perceived frequencies may vary on an average in the
ratio of 1:100,000 between the pianissimo of a murmur, and the
fortissimo of a bugle.

The immensity of this range results from the logarithmic functioning of the auditive receiver, which does not experience equal
differences between two frequencies or between two amplitudes
as equal intervals, but rather as equal rations. For example, it
has the same impression when passing from 100 to 200 c.p.s., a
difference of one hundred, as going from 1,000 to 2,000, a difference of one thousand, so that it appears only concerned with the
ratio 200:100, and then 2,000:1,000 which is 2 in both cases. The
smallest perceptible interval is called "savart" for frequencies, and
the decibel for amplitudes. The "savart" is 25 times smaller than
the semi-tone of the musicians' keyboard, since it divides the
octave into 300 intervals instead of the 12 which also occur in
dodecaphonic or atonal music. In piano tuning, for example,

the accuracy margins tolerated are 3 "savarts." As for the "decibel," it divides amplitude into 100 perceptible levels which may vary in the ratio of 1:100,000 on the average.

The average auditive receiver can discern 3,000 pitches of sounds or tones, with 100 vibratory amplitude levels in each of them. It may be compared to a passive piano with 3,000 cords marked from 0 to 3,000 savarts, each of which can vibrate by resonance up to an amplitude whose level is usually graduated between 0 and 100 decibels. It may also be compared to a comb with 3,000 teeth or vibrating blades. At all times the auditive spectrum indicates the cords or teeth which are starting to resonate, and their relative amplitudes. Although, according to Fourier, the infinite number of mathematical components has already been reduced to 3,000, it would nevertheless be difficult to construct a spectrograph giving the same data as the auditive apparatus. One would have to construct 3,000 mechanical resonators or electrical filters and have their amplitudes as a function of time inscribed by a 3,000-track oscillograph, which would thus be 500 times wider than that of the current six-track model. Its recording roll would be about 300 meters wide.

To return to the natural auditive receiver, its information capacity per fifteenth of a second is obtained by calculating all the possible combinations of the 3,000 cords and their 100 levels. Combinative analysis shows that this capacity, or the total number of discernible sounds S, is the number 100 multiplied by itself 3,000 times, which is the same as multiplying the number 10 by itself 6,000 times. One would need three whole pages covered with closely written zeros to write out $10^{6,000}$.

We can ask ourselves the following theoretical question: if the number of discernible levels were reduced from 100 to 3, or even to 2 per cord, how many cords would be required to still obtain the same number S of discernible sounds?

The theory of information gives the following answer:

$$S = 100^{3000} \text{ (savarts)} = 10^{6000} \text{ (DIT)} = 3^{12000} \text{ (TIT)} = 2^{20000} \text{ (BIT)}$$

We can thus choose at will from among the following equivalent information: either 3000 cords with 100 levels, or "savarts," in the natural auditive system (on the basis of 100), or 6000 cords with 10 levels, termed DIT or decimal digit, in the decimal system (basis 10),

or 12000 cords with 3 levels, termed TIT, or ternary digit, in the ternary system (basis 3),

or 20000 cords with 2 levels, termed BIT or binary digit, in the binary system (basis 2).

In the latter case, each one of the 20000 cords could only either vibrate or not vibrate: its answer would be all or nothing, yes or no, and it constitutes the unit of information or BIT used by technicians, though it is the DIT which is best adapted to our decimal system.

In any case, we can dispense with all scientific terms, and simply speak of zeros. Thus when he has to characterise high orders of numbers, the man of today will advantageously replace the terms "thousands," "millions," "billions," by "three zeros," "six zeros," "nine zeros," which enables him to do logarithmic calculations without knowing it. Regarding the auditive information-receiving capacity, or number of sounds discernible in a fifteenth of a second, we know that it is a "six thousand zero." Expressed thus this number is easier to assimilate. It remains immense, however, when compared with the total number of all the particles of the universe, which is estimated to be less than a "hundred zero."

If each phonetic element, vowel or consonant, could be emitted individually between two silences, the problem would be relatively simple. In fact, since Helmholtz, we have known about the mechanism of the emission of vowels in continuous sequence. Let us summarize, for example, the emission of the "i." The vocal cords emit sawtoothed vibrations rich in harmonics. If the fundamental or lowest frequency is 150 c.p.s., or approximately that of D_2 sharp, its spectrum indicates amplitude bars decreasing to 300 c.p.s. (D_3 sharp), 450 c.p.s. (A_3 sharp), 600 c.p.s. (D_4 sharp) and so on. These harmonics excite certain oral resonances, or cavities "formed" by the mouth in order to articulate a given sound. In a general manner, the regions of frequency characteristic of a sound are called "formants." The formants of the "i" are two in number, circa 3000 c.p.s. (D_3 sharp) excited by harmonic number 2 and circa 2850 c.p.s. (F_6 sharp), excited by harmonic number 19 and its neighbours. By modifying the pitch of the masculine or feminine fundamental, which can vary between 86 c.p.s. (F_1) and 384 c.p.s. (G_3) approximately, the harmonic numbers are greatly displaced, but the mouth cavities little so; thus it is approximately the same formants, termed "quasi-fixed," which are excited by other harmonics. Their regions are very indefinite because of the softness of the walls of the mouth and the inevitable fluctuations in the pitch of the voice.

In addition, the auditive receiver greatly distorts the spectrum emitted, firstly because its curve of equal sensitivity favorises certain frequencies as the increase, up to about 3,000 c.p.s. (G_6), and secondly because of its logarithmic response to amplitude.

In 1952 the prototype I of the Phonetograph was based on this principle. The theoretical discrimination of $2^6 = 64$ or $3^6 = 81$ different sounds was obtained by connecting to each filter, relays which distinguish 2 or 3 amplitude levels. But in practice it was only able to separate 12 vowels or dipthongs and 5 consonants. It refused, for example, to distinguish the plosives (P,K,T) from the fricatives (S, CH, F), the unvoiced from the voiced (B,G,D or Z,J,V), these from the vowels (U,E,I), the N's from the M's and L's, and the O's from the R's. It was unable to split up a word into its phonetic elements, except for a few combinations of vowels with three consonants (L,S,CH).

There was one decisive reason for this: the prototype I had no subformants nor levellers and followers. We had to await prototypes II and III to discover the missing elements of information: the subformants appeared in 1956 and in 1961 the levellers and followers.

In order to familiarize the reader with these new notions of the physics of language, we will here undertake the study of the train of waves which carries the word *Novelti*, as it would appear on an oscilloscope screen. We see the carrying wave symbolized by a modulated sinusoid. We have some knowledge of its quasi-stationary components in the area marked off by horizontals. In fact, the spectrum of the "i" has revealed that it is a question of a mixture of frequencies falling mainly between 100 and 6,000 c.p.s. whose dominants, termed *formants,* are very simple.

On the other hand, we do not see how the sound "t" could be distinguished from the sound "i" to which it seems inseparably joined. However, the oblique lines linking the horizontals show slight differences in slope. This leads us to analyse the envelope of the train of waves, that is the *carrying wave*. Such an analysis was long considered as a waste of time since, according to some specialists, its spectrum would only add very low frequencies, with very weak amplitudes, to which the ear is practically insensible. However, the analyser of the Phonetograph, prototype II, showed in 1956 that the spectrum of the envelope, or more precisely of the variation of formant, could furnish a new category of frequencies located between 16 and 76 c.p.s., the *subformants,* enabling the plosive consonants, P,K,T, fricatives CH,F,S, the rolled R's and the glides in general to be identified.

However, the formant levels were falsified by the weakness of the consonants in relation to the vowels, and by other irregularities. In fact, even though the "V" is as important as the "E" information wise, its general level is far weaker. The balancing of these diversities necessitated the construction of a sonemic compressor or leveller. "Soneme" is the term used to define all elements of sound to be identified. The sonemic compressor is an amplifier whose gain is variable in function of amplitude and frequency, in accordance with two distinct laws, in such a way as to equalize the levels of a group of sonemes to be distinguished. At 100 c.p.s., for example, the input level V_{in} varies from 0.1 to 1, or a hundredfold whereas the output level V_{out} goes from 0.1 to 0.2, or twofold. Therefore, its compression ratio is $100:2 = 50$. On the contrary, at 200 c.p.s., the output level varies from 0.2 to 4 and the compression ratio has fallen to $100:20 = 5$. We know that the domain of the fundamental, from 100 to 400 approximately, contributes but little to the compression, which is controlled above all by the harmonics. It is then a question of a compression that is selective in frequency. We must also note that the compressions are not produced instantaneously but that they require a certain time T_1 to establish themselves. Also a sudden overtaking may occur or—on the other hand—momentary lack. Technics will enable any desired weight of compression to be obtained, but we need not concern ourselves with the details here.

It is sufficient to note that our train of waves which was very irregular at the emission, seems to have passed through rollers which have each soneme approximately the same overall level. Thus having got rid of its parasitic variations of level, the wave is analysed by some ten formant filters ranging, for instance, between 200 and 6,000 c.p.s. which, after rectification and filtering from 0 to 16 c.p.s., furnish slow variations of amplitude termed *quasi-fixed formants*. We thus dispose of ten initial elements of information. It is sufficient to choose two or three levels (0,1,2,) in order to identify the *quasi-stationary* parts, termed "*statemes*," of vowels such as O, E, I, or continuant consonants such as N, V, L.

As for the subformants, they are obtained as follows: the partial waves furnished by the formant filters are rectified from 0 to 76 c.p.s., then their initial variation and final variation are themselves analysed by subformant filters which are situated circa 30 and 60 c.p.s. These furnish a further score of elements of information, only two or three levels of which need be chosen in order to identify the transitory parts of the sonemes termed "*transemes*" (for example, the entry of the vowels O, E, I, or the plosive consonants P, K, T, or the fluctuations of V).

Between 1957 and 1959, the first part of the Phonetograph prototype III was constructed on these principles and tested.

But the following difficulties were encountered:

a) The sonemic compressor or leveller modified the subformants. Several levellers should have been provided, adapted to different groups of vowels or consonants instead of a single one.

b) The more accurate the leveller the more marked, depending on the quality of the speaker's voice, were the intervals between the formants which are only quasi-fixed. An automatic formant corrector in function of the voice pitch should have been provided.

c) The strike of the typewriter keys was not synchronized with succession of the sonemes. In fact, their phases were controlled and auto-repeated by the formants alone.

A second clock or time scale t (sec) measuring the intervals between subformants, should have been provided in order to obtain the rhythm of succession of the sonemes. Lastly, it was impossible to distinguish between the voiced consonants and the voiceless ones.

In any procession of sounds, be it musical or linguistic, the auditive receiver is able to distinguish five categories of elements of information: intonation, harmony, noise, rhythm, and melody.

Intonation was covered by the automatic control of the leveller together with the other parasitic variations in level. But at the time it cancelled itself out from the purely phonetic information.

Harmony (such as the timbre of the vowels) is effectively selected with the aid of some ten formants, at least for a given voice.

Noise, which characterises the entry of the sonemes and their fluctuations, had also been identified with the help of some twenty subformants.

Rhythm can be furnished by means of a timing device that actuates the typewriter keys and is synchronized with these same subformants.

Melody, which first disappeared with the lost voice, was finally found in a mobile region of low frequencies which follows the fundamental at a distance of few semitones. It is of very low amplitude although very energetic compared with other sonemes. This region is called the region of *"follower-formants."* At one and the same time it enabled us to spot the melody, which above all is conspicuous by its absence, because it is generally drowned in the first quasi-fixed formants.

The Phonetograph, prototype IV, will thus be equipped with some twenty so-called *"mobile formants"* ranging from 76 to 344 c.p.s. There will automatically be two follower-formants among them, located just below the fundamental. They will express the melody of the fundamental while adjusting the vowel filters and supplying the missing information on the consonants.

If we look attentively at the quasi-stationary spectrum of the "i," we realize that the fundamental at 150 c.p.s. is not distinguished by its formants but by the weakness of the frequencies immediately below it. Comparatively, the regions have higher amplitudes at the time of the glide, that is to say at the time of the entry of the "i." It is consequently plausible that plosive or fricative consonants will produce interesting phenomena at this point. One thing should be mentioned: in the case of musical analysis, the mobile formants can rise parallel to the quasi-fixed ones up to the 16,000 c.p.s. limit. Indeed, the resonances of various musical instruments, such as the flute, are displaced with the fundamental.

The elements of information of spoken language are far more complex than those of a single musical instrument. Their resonances derive from the violin, in their quasi-fixed formants from the flute, in their followers, from the drum, in their sub-formants and so on. However, the Phonetograph, prototype IV, in eliminating the greater part of the 3,000 intervals of frequency, of the 100 levels and the six thousand zeros of possible sounds, has greatly contributed to the solution of this important problem in auditive cybernetics. There remain only some 100 elements of information, and two or three levels. They are sufficient, nonetheless, to feed a whole host of analogic or numerical functions. It is in this way that the control elements of these levellers, for example, furnish *decibelgraphs* which indicate the dynamics or general level between pianissimo or fortissimo, or the speakers intonation or emotion.

The *statigraph*, emanating from the quasi-stationary parts of the sonemes, can be divided into *harmographs* or *melographs*, depending on whether they are linked to mobile or quasi-fixed formants. They can give as much information as may be required about the harmony or the melody, about the vowels and the contituants, and about the timbre or the personality of the speaker.

The *transigraphs* emanating from the subformants not only characterize the plosive, fricative and rolled consonants, but also the rhythm of succession of the sonemes. They thus furnish *rhythmographs*.

We can attempt to explain in a more visual and concrete manner how the Phonetograph functions by transposing the world of sounds into that of colours. In examining the analogy between sounds and colours more closely, it is important to note that the figures that follow will only be orders of magnitude.

If the eye looks at a sheet of paper corresponding to the visual field, its (linear) separating power on a vertical column is such that it can distinguish up to approximately 3000 parallel strokes.

The ear can distinguish approximately 3000 levels of sound between the lowest note and the shrillest one. The number of colours or hues that the eye can readily distinguish is around 100 between red and violet. As for the ear, it can discern some 100 levels of sound intensity between the pianissimo of a murmur and the fortissimo of a trumpet. The (linear) information capacity of the eye on a vertical column is thus similar to that of the ear, or: $2^{20,000(BIT)}$ per element of time discernible, that is per fifteenth of a second on the average for the ear. This vast figure represents the maximum number of linear images and sounds between which a correspondence can be established.

In order to explain the auditive analysis done by the *Phonetograph*, we can make a table showing the correspondences between the range of auditive frequencies and the range of colour frequencies. The fundamental or melody of the human voice, which can vary between 80 and 400 c.p.s., is represented by a score of red hues ranging from dark to light; next, the range of the harmonics, from 400 to 6,000 c.p.s., is split up into nine frequency bands "quasi-fixed formants" which are represented by nine colours of the rainbow, from orange to ultramarine blue—as in the following table:

Funda-mental Melody		*Quasi-fixed Formants Harmony*							
dark red to light red	orange	orange/ yellow	yellow	lemon yellow	yellow/ green	green	blue/ green	blue	ultramarine blue
80 to 400 c.p.s.	400-600	600-800	800-1200	1200-1600	1600-2000	2000-2400	2400-2800	2800-3200	4000-6000

If the train of auditive waves representing, for example, the word NOVELTI could be coloured and passed in front of a telescope it would appear as a series of small clouds lit up against a night sky background.

In fact, phonetic emission can be transposed optically as follows: the vocal cords emit a white light which thus contains a mixture of all colours. Now the buccal or other cavities, "formed" by the speaker when he wishes to articulate a sound, colour this white light as a result of resonances. This colouration corresponds to the quasi-fixed formants which determine the individual timbre of each vowel or quasi-stationary consonant. For example, O is orange-tinged and the V blue-tinged.

The unaided ear is capable of splitting up each complex sound and recognizing the pure component sounds. On the contrary, the eye requires an artificial auxiliary such as a spectroscope prism to be able to recognize pure colours in a mixture of colours. Thus, in order to "see" the physiology of the *Phonetograph* which imitates the human ear, we shall consider it as a prism which splits up impure colours into their constituent elements.

The purplish-blue of the N is formed of different spectrum rays than the purplish-blue of the I.

The quasi-stationary spectra of the phonetic elements, fewer than a hundred in number, are to some degree analogous to a few of the visible spectra among the 92 atomic elements.

In addition, a coherent luminous wavetrain emanating from an atom lasts, for example, for a hundredth of a micro-second and is propagated at a speed of 300,000 kilometers per second. Its observable length is thus three meters. Now an auditive wave period emanating from a speaker whose voice is pitched at 110 c.p.s., lasts nine milliseconds and is propagated at a speed of 330 meters per second. Its observable length is thus also three meters.

In the description of the *Phonetograph* we must now consider the last unknown, so to speak, the mechanism of information which sets off the desired keys of the typewriter, mechanism which transforms word into action and the procedure of which is called "*phonaction.*" This mechanism involves coding and matrix technics which it would be tedious to describe in detail here. At any rate, we can imagine a model which in practice combines not only these technics, but also combinative analysis, the theory of information and various abstract notions of physics, such as entropy, vectorial calculus, and the transformation of coordinates: this is the cylinder lock (Fig. 34 a and b).

According to Figure 34a, the cylinder Z can only be rotated on its axis A-A when the proper key S_1 has displaced all five blocking

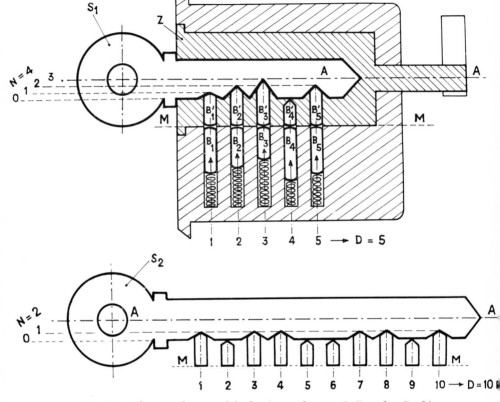

FIG. 34. Phonetic keys and locks (according to J. Dreyfus-Graf.)

Left: The cylinder lock as a model of communication theory.

Number of blocking pins or teeth $D = 5$ with $N = 4$ possible levels each.

Number of possible combinations $N^D = 4^5 = 1024$.

Right: Equivalent cylinder lock with $N = 2$ levels for each pin or tooth.

Number of pins $D = 10$ (bits).

Number of possible combinations $N^D = 2^{10} = 1024 \ (=4^5)$.

pin pairs B_1-B_1' to B_5-B_5' against their springs in order that the contact surfaces between each pin pair is aligned with the surface M-M of the cylinder.

If only one pin pair were used with $N = 4$ possible heights or levels we could have $K = 4$ different combinations of locks and keys. If $D = 2$ pin pairs were used the number of combinations is K $= 4^2 = 16$. According to Fig. 34, D $= 5$ and N $= 4$; consequently K $=$ N^D $= 4^5 = 1024$ combinations.

Communication theory is more interested in the total number of combinations than in the internal composition of levels and pins, exactly as in the cylinder lock. The unit of information is a key tooth with N $= 2$ possible levels (zero-one or yes-no). It is called a bit (short expression for binary digit): the keys of Figure 34 correspond to equal information quantities. This means 10 bits.

The analogy could be additionally extended. For example, the noise level could be expressed by the mechanical play or back lash. For our present study it is enough to imagine the following: the important frequency components called "formants" of sound waves are analysed by a number D of filters which correspond to the number of teeth on the key. In each filter or teeth we can distinguish N amplitude levels. The maximum number of distinguishable sounds or locks is N^D. If we can identify 1:T different sounds per second and if D is expressed in bits (this means the level number is reduced to N $= 2$), the information capacity becomes C $= DT$ bits/sec.

The block is called the *matrix* of the Phonetograph. This matrix contains 30 vertical locks termed phonetic elements and which are locked by the black segments of the 18 transversal axes known as formants and subformants. Likewise, each key is equipped with 18 prongs of three levels; each time that one of the keys encounter its corresponding combination in the block, it liberates one and only one rod, which strikes the required letter (Fig. 34).

The human ear contains a sixthousandzeros total of locks, each of which can be opened by an acoustical key having a specific combination of 3000 prongs and 100 levels. A teleprinter makes do with 32 locks which can be operated by minute keys of five prongs and two levels. The *Phonetograph* comprises virtually 400 million locks of which only 30-odd are used to discern the phonetic elements and each key has up to 18 prongs of three levels. The wastage of such a machine is striking when compared to the economy of a teleprinter. But the *Phonetograph* is half-way between the machine and life—and the prodigality of life is unbounded.

VECTOGRAPH AND ORIENTATIVE
CYBERNETICS

As we can see, the cochlea and its cybernetic model, the *Phonetograph,* are only transformers of information: their role is firstly that of codifying, in physiological language, an ondulatory informative language. The vestibule and its first cybernetic model, the *Electronic Vectograph,* go further: above the codification of information there is an action of corrective regulation in relation to tolerances previously determined; (these tolerances can be shown, for instance, in angular degrees of oscillation around a median vertical axis of the body in orthostatic position, around a horizontal axis in lateral or dorsal decubitus). We see directly why the cybernetics of the vestibular apparatus, which we are the first to have attempted, is infinitely more complex than that of the cochlea.

We will discuss briefly, then, in this chapter, some elements of a possible solution to a problem which is, as we have said, double: first, as in cochlear cybernetics, an *informational analysis* of the applied stimulus followed by a *regulating reaction.*

The cupula, that internal exteroceptor, makes up only one part of a vast whole in the sensorial labyrinthine complex: the role of the otoliths, at least in superior animals, have not up to now been the object of a precise functional definition. We will therefore limit our study to the semicircular canals, about which we have considerable information. We can summarize the problem of informational analysis in the four points that follow:

1. Response or absence of response to a measurable and reproducible stimulus: we define in this way the *reactivity* of the vestibulary apparatus, a notion which can end with the definition of a *threshold of excitability* in determined conditions.

2. Translation of directional information furnished by an adequate, measurable and reproducible stimulus: we

162

define in this way a *directional sensibility* of the vestibulary apparatus, a notion which can end in the definition of the *thresholds of directional sensibility* in determined conditions.

3. Translation of the intensity of the information furnished by a measurable stimulus: we define in this manner a capacity for information of the vestibulary apparatus, a notion which can end in the definition of a *minimal information threshold* independent of the nature of the applied stimulus but depending uniquely on the duration of its application.

4. Qualification and quantification of secondary sources of information. We thus define an *interferential information*, a notion which results in the definition of a *threshold of general information* depending on the nature and respective duration of application of diverse secondary stimuli concomitant with the adequate primary stimulus.

Let us note that several authors have undertaken, for several years, to determine, in often diverse conditions, the values of some of the thresholds of which we have been speaking. The most remarkable of these works is that of Montandon for points 1) and 2), Hennebert sr. for point 3); lastly, the phenomena of *vestibulary audition* has been the object of research made by Bocca

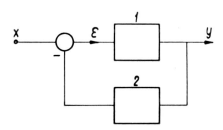

Fɪɢ. 35. Physical schema of a transfer of signals in an automatic regulation (according to Loeb).
1. mechanism.
2. control loop.
x. input signal.
y. output signal.

and more recently by Dittrich and Dreyfus-Graf. The most notable result of this last research is the discovery that the labyrinth receives the envelope of the carrying wave without demodulating it: the demodulation is effected by the cochlea which thus rediscovers the frequencies of the carrying wave (70-16000 Hz).

It is clear that if the first two points of the problem are easy to treat in binary and ternary combinations, it is quite the opposite for the point dealing with the translation of intensity. We point out that this point is also disputed in auditive cybernetics. Thus the conclusions drawn by Hennebert are not lacking in interest to confine the question to its true limits; this author says in effect that: ". . . the cupular system is a perfect accelerometer in normal conditions; but it is activated only when weak accelerations and long periods of time are applied to it." There is every reason to think that, for parameters that are inverse (short time and strong acceleration), the translation of intensity is perturbed in such a way that the cupular system acts as a simple goniometer. The works of Di Giorgio, confirmed by recent histological research by Borghesan on the delicate structure of the reticulary zone of the "planum semilunatum," as well as our personal research on the perstimulatory cupular metamorphism permit us to assert that the notion of intensity is translated by the duration of the primary oscillation (perstimulatory) of the cupule endolymph interface; thus a stimulation of very long duration (450 sec) and very feeble rotatory acceleration $(0.2^\circ/s^2)$ produces a secondary oscillation (poststimulatory, that is to say consecutive with a brusk halt in the stimulation) more violent than that produced by a briefer stimulation (90 seconds) of superior accelerometric intensity $(1^\circ/s^2)$. One can thus rupture the cupulary membrane in two manners: the same effect produced by two different causes, first following the sudden interruption of a very long stimulation of weak intensity, secondly by a sudden depression of the membrane consecutive with a stimulation of very strong intensity but short duration. These observations superpose themselves on those made in the field of sound traumatisms.

As to the fourth point, that of secondary afferences, we have already studied the anatomical connections in the beginning of this book: these connections justify the denomination that we have proposed for the posterior labyrinth as general *receptor of orientation.*

The anatomical description is not sufficient for understanding the functional description; the possible rudiments of the solution of the cybernetic problem for the vestibular apparatus are summed up in the construction of efficient functional models. It does not seem that the so-called "physical" models made up to now, such as those of Steinhausen (Traegheitskompass) or of Groen (torsion swing), can take into account all the properties of the cupular receptor. Only the first two types of information listed above and their possible translation, expressed by a function which one supposes *a priori* to be linear, are explainable by such models: the *reactivity* and the *directional sensitivity* of the receptor. But the notion of intensity escapes them. There is no doubt however on what is known as the "Ewald's second law," primarily a hydrodynamic principle which became a neurophysiological principle following the remarkable work on the part of histologists (Ramon Y Cajal, Di Giorgio, Dohlmann, Borghesan) and electronystagmographists (Montandon *et coll.*, Ferreri *et coll.*), founders of modern *vestibulometry.* A remarkable restatement of this problem, which certain persons believed a thorny one, has been made recently by Guettich, of Munich.

Upon solid experimental foundations, as often direct as indirect, a predominance of the physiological stimulatory action of the endolymphatic ampullopetal current on the ampullofugal current, has been shown. Allow us to add, however, that the study by indirect proofs (electronystagmography) should only be undertaken under very precisely determined experimental conditions, conditions to which we have already referred, for it is common scientific knowledge that the nystagmic reaction is vestibular only under these conditions. The thesis that P. Montandon Jr. maintained at the Physiology Institute of the University of Basle under the direction of Professor M. Monnier brings to this matter important complements of information on the cybernetic problem: the nystagmus itself is conditioned, we have already said, by the nystagmogenic diencephalic area described and localized in 1958 by Lachmann, Bergmann and Monnier. The influence of the

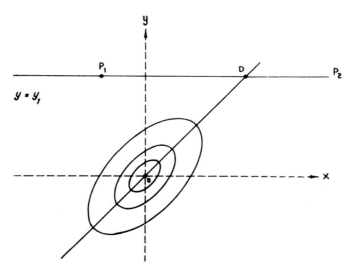

FIG. 36. Search for an optimum by the representation of the figurative
volume by a function: $ax^2 + bxy + cy^2$. (According to Loeb.)

vestibular apparatus on the reactions of this center is determined
like a relay which is or is not put into action under certain conditions of stimulation, in which case the consecutive nystagmic reaction is of *vestibular origin.* It is quite evident, however, that in
a great number of circumstances, notably in pathology, defects of
functioning of this relay engender nystagmic reactions for which
an important responsibility devolves upon central influences. A
recent statistical study by Pignataro and Dittrich and another one
by Dittrich and Maurizi better bring out how only the study of
the perrotatory nystagmus, as opposed to the postrotatory nystagmus and the sensation of rotation, is susceptible to yielding the
only valid criteria for a study of vestibulocentral interferences. In
fact, the current problem under study in our laboratory, of the *vis-
ualization* of perstimulatory endolymphatic currents is the last
obstacle to be overcome for the establishment of a "physical"
model of the cupular receptor.

What is left is to envisage the creation of a model which effi-
ciently comprehends the "unknowns" mentioned previously, that
is which translates the notions of intensity and secondary information also, but which can translate at the same time the respec-

tive interaction of the three semicircular canals without limiting itself to describing what is happening at the level of only one of these canals: we arrive in this manner at the notion familiar to the physiologist: that of the *homeostasy* of a system of regulation.

The *Electronic Vestograph* is derived from a first prototype intended for micromanipulations and presented in that primitive form at the first International Ergonomic Association Congress at Stockholm in 1961. This prototype (with thermoresistances) permitted the recording and the immediate reading of different cinetic vectors characterizing a micromovement of high frequency and very low amplitude. The fundamental relations of the mechanics allows the experimenter moreover to calculate, or to have calculated by an electronic computer, the desirable complementary vectors. A differentiator of the Powners and Lion type was the principal element of graphic information. The adaptation of various automation mechanisms brought the rudimentary descriptive conception to a stage of *action,* this term being understood here in the sense in which it was used for the *Phonetograph,* that is in opposition to the simple descriptive analysis of movements; in other words, by an affectation of furnished elements by this analysis to their autocorrection as a function of tolerances that are predetermined. The creation of such a model this amounts to an important first step on the road to the proper cybernetic solution of the vestibulary function.* It will be difficult for the reader whose formation has not dealt with such questions to penetrate immediately to the heart of a subject which is so complex. For this reason we will now retrace some important steps in the theory of automatic control, thus throwing more light on the first conclusions we have reached.

We know that one can decompose a mathematical function into two categories of elementary functions corresponding to two systems of reference: harmonic functions, with the frequency as reference, and the impulses, with the time as reference. These modes of decomposition lead to two types of analysis which are complementary, each one throwing light on a particular aspect of the phenomena considered: *harmonic analysis* and *impulses analysis.*

Note: Dittrich has realized a transducer-manometer which can be easily considered as a correct electro-mechanical analogous of the cupular system.

One can carry the parallelism between the two modes of analysis very far. In calculation the harmonic components of a function correspond the calculation of the values of the said function for the different value-units of its independent variable. There exists however a fundamental difference between these two modes of analysis.

In fact, thanks to the transformations made by Laplace and modern theories of distributions developed by Schwartz, the operational calculus, an extension of harmonic analysis, answers all the needs of mathematical rigor. On the other hand, impulses analysis, as it has been defined, particularly by Cuenod *et coll.*, is a method of approximate calculation of which the exactitude depends in particular on the value chosen as a unit of the independent variable. An improvement of the exactitude can be obtained in reducing the value of this unit, resulting at the same time in an increase in the volume of the calculations. Another difference resides in the fact that impulses analysis gives the result of the calculation in the form of a series of values and not in the form of an analytic expression. At the same time, the results thus furnished in numerical form have the advantage of being usable immediately; for the "theoretic" exactitude of the mathematician, the engineer substitutes a "practical" exactitude, which corresponds to an optimum understanding of certain limitations, due principally to the impression of the measurement of numeric values arising in the calculations, to the simplifying hypotheses necessitated by the putting of the problem into equation form, to the restrictions imposed by the execution of the calculations and to the tolerances allowed in the utilization of the results. Applied to the servomechanism theory, harmonic analysis, thanks to the use of Nyquist's criteria and other related criteria, which we have mentioned in the third portion of this work, is particularly suitable for the determination of conditions of stability of automatic regulation. On the other hand, the impulses analysis is very advantageous for the calculation of the variations of the size to be regulated resulting from a pertubation of speed of some sort affecting the regulation. The perspectives opened by arithmetic computers speak in favor of impulses analysis, for this method of

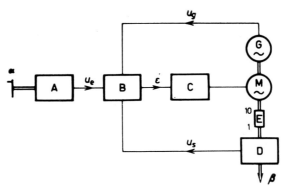

FIG. 37. Schema of an assemblage for the regulation of position (according to Luedi).

A = generator (threshold tension).
B = additions unit.
C = amplifier.
M = motor.
E = machine unit.
D = generator (activity tension).
U_e = input tension of the system = $U_e = f(t)$.
U_g = tachodynamometric tension = $U_g = f(n)$.
U_s = output tension of the D generator = $U_s = f(B)$.
E = variation of the controlled tension = $E = U_e - U_g - U_s$.
u = motor tension.
M_d = motor momentum.
n = r/p/m of the motor.
(Tension in volts.)

calculation in series lends itself especially well to their use. The method answers the wish expressed by Couffignal:

"In the same way as powerful modern machines determine the organization of work in a shop that uses mechanical manufacturing methods, computing machines are powerful enough today to become the element upon which the organization of calculation itself is based; machines and methods react to one another profoundly; organization and mechanization must be studied together and one for the other."

We are at the present time experiencing an extreme generalization of the notion of feed-back, the best synthesis of this rate of

things can be represented in the schema shown below where the
mechanism is the data of the problem. It is up to the cybernetician to arrange the organs of the feed-back loop in such a way as
to reproduce the physiological servomechanism in its effects.
The steps to be taken in this respect become concrete through the
values of a certain number of parameters measurable by the ex-
perimenters and of which the cybernetician will retain those
which the creation of his model necessitate.

One would like to systematize and render automatic the
search for the entirety of the values of the parameters x_1, x_2
. . . . . .x_n giving a function f $(x_1, x_2 . . . . . .x_n)$ a priori, which will
be, for example, a reaction time or a quantity of information which
one would like to render either as small as possible or as large as
possible. The work presents no mathematical difficulties if one
knows the function f (x) either in the form of an analytic expression or in the form of an empiric table of values. The technic of
models permits, in representing the mechanism by an entirety
of mechanisms, most often electric, the restitution of the functioning with a scale of suitable times. The search for an extremum
is made by successive tentatives that should be systematized. As
soon as the representative point has penetrated into the region of
space where the function f (x) can without too much error be
represented by a development in series stopping at the 2nd degree, following the increasing powers of x, calculated with the
extremum itself taken as origin of the coordinates:

$$f (x_1,x_2 . . . . . .x_n) = f_0 + a_{11} x_1^2 + ...a_{12}x_1x_2 + ...$$

One can imagine many sure methods founded on the known properties of the matrix *aij*. If one wishes to represent things by a
figure, one must limit oneself to the case of two variables. Traced
here, following in the neighbourhood of the minimum, are the
gauge lines of the paraboloid: $\xi = ax^2 + 2bxy + cy^2$. This is a
family of homothetic ellipses. Let us start from P_1 and let us find
the value of which, for a constant value of y, or y_1, renders the
side z minimal. The point D thus obtained is on the right conju-
gate of the axis of the x in relation to the ellipses. This simple tentative step already gives a fundamental result in the quadratic
(formula as above). It is not difficult to see how one can con-

tinue, in systematizing the study, in such a way as to surely reach zero. It is a question of knowing if the manoeuvre effected on one of the parameters x_n, has as effect the increase or diminution of the function f.

The regulation of position is besides one of the principal application of automatics; it consists in transmitting, analogically or digitally, any geometric information in order to reproduce it at a determined location and to control the exactitude of that reproduction. Its utilization, current in industry, is also met in metrological telecommunication and, under this heading, will allow the reader to understand its importance as a cybernetic approach to the labyrinthic sensorial receptor. In the chosen example, the system of regulation is conceived so that the angle $\propto$ chosen by the operator (or by the stimulus) will be represented at the exit in the form of an angle $\beta = \propto$. The consigned value u_s of the regulation of position is furnished, through a demultiplier, by a group motor-generator; it is then compared to the threshold value u_e. As long as there is not a perfect superposition in the chosen margin of tolerances, the two angular values furnished by the block-transmitter threshold A and the block-transmitter of the consigned value D, one will obtain an error tension ξ from which one subtracts the value of the *dynamotachymetric tension* u_g. In other words the error tension ξ adds on to a value determined as normal for the tension u_g for which $\xi = 0$. The difference obtained in case of divergence is amplified and creates at the level of the motor a couple M_d, due to which the consigned value is modified until the point where the equality of the threshold and consigned values are once more achieved. Then the motor stops.

It is interesting to note in passing that a solution of the same order, but applied to the correction of speeds, guides the automatic control of the *Liminary Girograph* by Montandon and Dittrich. But it is obviously only a related technic, without any cybernetic relation.

The first cybernetic approach to the cupular sensorial receptor shows us, besides its positive elements of solution that it is susceptible to bring, how an apparently insoluble problem can be approximated by devious paths. The great German physiologist

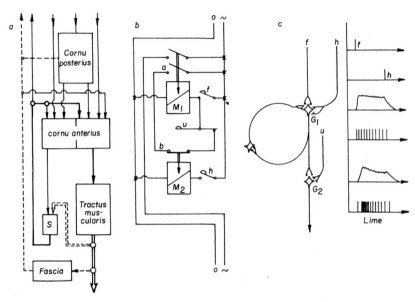

Fig. 38. Motor regulation (according to Ranke).
a) schema of assemblage.
b) physical graph.
c) physiological graph.

Ranke has shown sufficiently that neurophysiology was certain to make no progress if it limited its information only to histoanatomical and biochemical data. Cybernetics, taking other "paths" than those described by morphologists, reach better and less questionable conclusions since they represent the experimental facts themselves, identical effects coming from analogous causes by different roads. In this line, it is now indispensable to make the parallel of the model proposed by Ranke to describe the exteroceptive reflex arc with the model that we have just described for the regulation of position. We will thus advance a step further in our investigation which, remember, intends to furnish elements for a solution and not a definitive description.

One can see in the following schemas, borrowed from Ranke, that the exciter fiber f frees, with the help of a single action potential, a local excitation of the ganglion cell G_1, an excitation which continues in the circuit with the help of auxiliary ganglion cells until the moment when the inhibitor fiber h cuts the excitation of the circuit also with the help of a single action potential.

The local erethysm of the ganglion cell G_2 is maintained by the bombarding of action currents coming from G_1; this erethysm in turn maintains the action potentials of the efferent fiber. An inhibitor fiber u in G_2 can prevent this erethysm in G_2 despite the bombardments coming from G_1 but only during the time of action of the fiber u. One can see in the electric graph that the relay f closes the magnetic induction circuit at M_1 as long as the double interrupter a is closed. The circuit is then closed at a-b-u and the electromagnet is attracted downward until the time when, in touching the button u, the operator opens the circuit in such a way that the electromagnet M_1 is shut off. But instead of this rupture at u, which takes into consideration the polarity of the magnet, one can also produce the starting up of M_2 by closing relay h: the consequence of this is the interruption of the circuit at b:, it represents too the inversion of polarity due to the inhibiting action of the fiber h.

The Ranke model is not satisfactory, however, for the solution we are searching for the vestibular receptor, for the very reason of the number of its variables. These as we had occasion to mention above, are essentially 4. We are thus faced with an information problem with 4 variables of which the matrix combination might be the following:

	A (1)	A (2)	A (3)	A (4)
B (1)	0	I	II	III
B (2)	I	II	III	0
B (3)	II	III	0	I
B (4)	III	0	I	II

This type of combination would be that established to command three lamps (I, II, III) successively and always in the same order, and their extinction (0), through two commutators situated in two different parts of a room, these commutators A and B would then be at 4 positions (0, I, II, IIII): the table of matrix combination shows 16 combinations, so A must be at a single stage at 4 positions (A(1), A(2), A(3), A(4)) and B at 3 stages at 4 positions, thus making the 12 combinations that remain. We could thus describe the 4 properties to define of a vestibular vector: existence or value of rest (0), active value (I), sense or directionality (II) and, on the condition that a binary system (yes or no) is retained, direction or angularity (III). One can conceive of the difficulties of the actual conditions if we explain that, contrary to the combinations proposed above, the experimental combinations do not follow in a determined order and moreover, are inter- and auto-correlative in certain conditions.

And too, the matrix table that precedes does not take into consideration more than a single "situation" at a time; we can only understand all the combinations, as we have in the *Electronic Vectograph*, by coming back to combined analysis in the same manner as we have already done in the *Phonetograph*, in progressively reducing the number or informative sources without distorting the attended general effect.

In concluding this picture of the present situation and the direction of the evolution of vestibular cybernetics, we do not want to neglect speaking of the very remarkable *electromechanic homeostat* so-called by Ross Ashby. This model specifies the conception of a 4 variable system that we have sketched in its most rudimentary form.

We can look at this apparatus as being a part A coupled with a part B (Fig. 39). Part A comprises four needles (with bobbins and potentiometers) reacting upon one another to create a 4 variable system of which the B values are the entries. A condition in A is defined by the position of the needles. Depending on exterior conditions and the entry, A can have as states of equilibrium either those where the needles are at the center of the dial or those at the extreme positions. Part B is essentially comprised of a relay which can be excited or not and four contacters with 25 plots (which are not all represented in the figure). Each position fixes the value of a resistance; thus B has 2.25.25.25.25 possible states, or a total of 781,250. For this system, envisaging A as entry, B was constructed in such a way that when the relay is

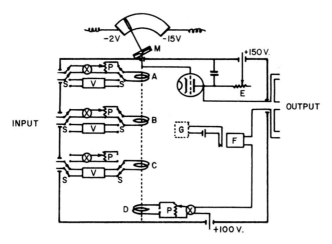

FIG. 39. Schema of an element of the electromechanical homeostat by Ashby. Four bobbins represent four influences of an element upon itself and four others. These influences come from tensions issuing from the liquid potentiometer of which the cursor is set into action by the equipment of galvanometer *M*. Reactions are effected either continuously by amplifier *V*, or discontinuously by uniselectors *X, X, X*.

fed none of *B's* states is a state of equilibrium (the contacters continue turning); on the contrary, when the relay is not fed, *B* is in equilibrium (the contacters are stopped). *B* and *A* are coupled in such a way that the relay is not fed, if and *only if A* is stable in the central position. As soon as a problem presents itself (that is to say when the value is modified by a parameter which is not represented on the figure), *A* possesses various possible states of equilibrium, and the whole takes a new state of equilibrium, implying that *B* too is in equilibrium. But we have just said that *B* is conceived in such a way that this does not happen except when the relay is not fed and the coupling of *A* and *B* only allows the cutting off of the feeding of the relay in the case where all the needles are at the center of their dials. Such a relation thus exempts all states of equilibrium in *A* where the needles are not in the center. In fact, we are dealing with "the trajectory of a system which evolves toward a state of equilibrium" and in this sense the homeostat does nothing else but attain this state of equilibrium.

Thus this machine, which is called the *electromechanical homeo-stat,* itself searches the solution of a definite problem in a series of actions, these ranging from impulses given by the needles to electric impulses introduced at any point in the circuit passing through exterior constraints for a connection, by use of a silk thread, between two adjacent needles. The machine idealizes well enough the concept that one can make *"vectaction,"* impulses being furnished by "affectors" such as microphones, photoelectric cells or sense organs. It makes a bridge, through the notion of *vectaction,* between the posterior labyrinth and its secondary af-ferences, particularly auditory and visual.

All the same, it would be presumptuous to consider the homeo-stat as a cybernetic model of the vestibulary sensorial apparatus. Research is not yet advanced enough today for anything else than patience and experimental integrity in the following up of works having such amplitude that they are not near being termi-nated. But it is important in such a new field to give the reader an idea of the questions being asked by those working on the problems, not in the way of idle speculations, but in the way fol-lowed by all analogical and digital machines themselves, that of the confrontation and successive elimination of logically incom-patible experimental facts.

FIRST ELEMENTS OF SYNTHESIS

As we have just said, Biophysics can not at the present time state proudly that it possesses a complete and definitive cochleo-vestibulary synthesis. In all related fields the most varied work likely to bring about this synthesis are under way. We mention here, among the most admirable, the recent tentative by Rassmunsen and Windle, who have just published *Neural Mechanisms of the Auditory and Vestibular Systems*, being supported by the most eminent collaborators.

These results, very encouraging, must not cause us to forget earlier and no less remarkable works of pioneer clinicians which bring the experimenter the fundamental data and sometimes even a salutary denial of speculations of an audacious nature.

At the same time we do not wish to neglect giving homage to the brilliant research of our master, Montandon, of Geneva, homage which includes a humble debt of gratitude for the formation, so precise and so enriching, that we owe him. Professor Montandon's numerous works, as founder of electronystagmographic vestibulometry with modern precision, are well enough known to permit our remembering him here. However, among his works we would like to mention the one which he devoted several years ago to *The Concordance Between Hearing Thresholds and Vestibulary Thresholds in Lesions of the Internal Ear*. This important monograph unquestionably constitutes one of the first tentatives of a systematic nature, according to criteria of a rigorously scientific spirit, of the difficult problem of the cochleo-vestibulary intercorrelations. If the conclusions drawn in this work are directed primarily toward clinical use, they have nonetheless the merit of opening the way for cyberneticians who as we know, are most often called upon to pronounce on the perfect functioning of a system, possessing only experimental data resulting from perturbations of this functioning.

We take the liberty of reproducing *in extenso* Montandon's conclusions which will thus introduce our own brief ones with which we end this work.

". . . The investigation of the concordance between the cochlear and vestibular thresholds obtained by means of the *liminal method of rotatory stimulation* applied to the study of 31 clinical cases of cochleo-vestibular lesions of peripheral origin has allowed us to establish the following correlations:

1. *In unilateral chronic otitis media* the vestibular threshold concords in general with the cochlear threshold as to the side of the lesion. Quantitatively however, the concordance between the two thresholds is only roughly true. Some discordances can be explained by compensation of central origin which tends after a few years to elevate the vestibular threshold of the sound side too. Lesions of the cochlear and vestibular receptors of the internal ear, which are very frequent and most often latent, can be demonstrated thanks to the newer methods of investigation by means of the elevation of the bone conduction threshold and by the concomitant elevation of the per-rotatory acceleratory nystagmic threshold. This syndrome constitutes a veritable "latent otitis interna" complicating most chronic otitis media.

2. *In bilateral chronic otitis* the concordance of the thresholds is less evident. It should be taken into consideration that the importance of the inflammation changes in the two parts of the labyrinth, the cochlear and the vestibular may be different in cases of partial or dissociated labyrinthitis. A unilateral latent nystagmus, only revealed by the labyrinthine stimulation, may lead to a wrong conclusion in case of a superficial examination.

3. *The fractures of the temporal bone* offer a typical example of a good concordance between the vestibular and cochlear thresholds when the lesions are unilateral. The electronystagmogram reveals also frequently signs of central origin due to the concussion, such as inhibition, or a directional preponderance of the nystagmus (Fig. 40).

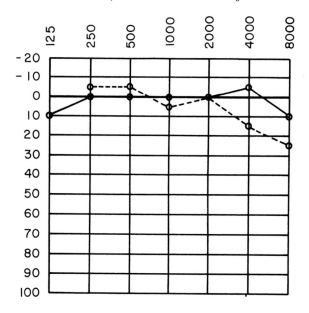

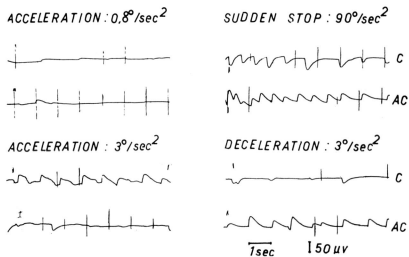

Fig. 40. Fracture of left temporal bone.
a) Audiogram: total deafness of left ear.
b) Vestibulogram: bilateral elevation of nystagmic threshold of acceleration above $1^0/s^2$; at $3^0/s^2$ the reaction appears at the right, whereas no
reaction appears at the left (L). After a sudden stop at $90^0/s$., the nystagmus occurs at the left as well as the right but the length of the reaction
at the left after a clockwise rotation is diminished. (According to Montandon.)

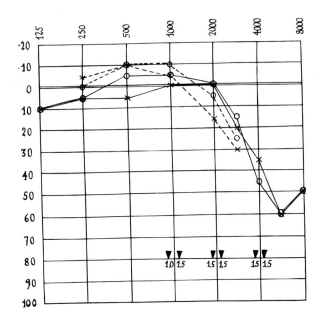

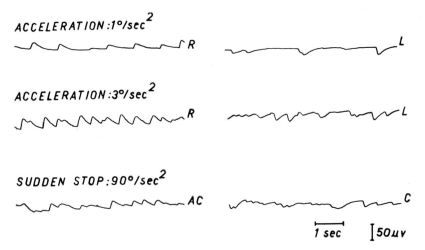

ACCELERATION: 1°/sec²

ACCELERATION: 3°/sec²

SUDDEN STOP: 90°/sec²

FIG. 41. Acoustical traumatism.
a) Audiogram: auditive hiatus at the left with contralateral effect and
   strengthening under the test of differential thresholds of amplitude.
b) Vestibulogram: slight elevation of nystagmic threshold of acceleration, above $1°/s^2$ to the left (L); at $3°/s^2$, the nystagmic reaction is net
   on both sides. (According to Montandon.)

4. *Even in certain acoustical traumas,* the liminal method of rotatory stimulation allows us to detach a slight elevation of the vestibular threshold which concords with the side and with the importance of the auditory hiatus (Fig. 41).

5. The results obtained by this method concord also with the audiometric results in *congenital cochleo-vestibular lesions.* These cases are especially interesting in the study of the compensation phenomena.

6. By comparing systematically the results obtained by means of the liminal method of rotatory stimulation with those due to the classical vestibular tests, it appears that:

a) The caloric tests are frequently doubtful as to their results, especially in cases of otitis media; furthermore, they may present a danger in cases of fractures of the temporal bone.

b) The tests based on the recording in the dark of the postrotational nystagmus after a sudden stop give frequently results which concord with those produced by the study of the nystagmic thresholds; their results are however not as clear and not as precise, especially in cases of central compensation or of a directional preponderance of the nystagmus.

c) *The spontaneous vestibular symptoms,* such as vertigo, deviations or nystagmus, are not present in general in cochleo-vestibular lesions of deficiency; these occasional signs are of little value, especially concerning the localization of the lesion."

EPITOME

In DRAWING TOWARD the concluding of this monograph consecrated to the biophysics of the ear, it is left for us to summarize provisionally our knowledge on the subject.

1. If it is true that the hearing part of the ear and all its annexes have been the object of numerous and varied works which greatly limit the unknowns, the same cannot be said for the orientative ear of which only a part of the sensorial mechanisms are known with certitude.

2. On the other hand, we can consider as acquired the essentials of the passages and of the anatomical topography of the two apparatuses, cochlear and vestibulary; morphology has brought and is bringing more light on to some points of detail without modifying anything essential in what is known about these organs.

3. In the same way, the strictly biophysical study of the cochlear ear can be considered as well defined and exempt from major ulterior difficulties. On the other hand, we do not yet know with enough precision which role the otolithes play in the vestibulary ear. We have not yet been able to establish, as has been done for the cochlear ear, the nature of the endolymphatic currents and the mode of vibration of the membrane which is consecutive with them; at least the works undertaken up to now have given only qualitative or grossly quantitative indications.

4. Finally, one can also consider auditive cybernetics as approaching its goal whereas vestibulary cybernetics is still held back in its development by the absence or imprecision of certain direct experimental data relative to the actual functioning of the sensorial mechanism and to the difficulty of translating its localization or

expressing clearly the nature of its quantum of information.

It is, however, incontestable that the growing interest that is attached to the vestibulary function in all fields will have as its consequence, in the near future, the coordination of efforts of diverse origin necessary for the solution of the problems which are still to be solved, for, as Bacon has said:

> "Science is nothing else than the image of Truth. The truth of being and the truth of knowing are one and the same thing, and differ no more among themselves than the direct ray and the reflected ray."

SELECTED REFERENCES

Bard, Ph.: *Medical Physiology*, Mosby, St. Louis (1956).

Bekesy, von, G.: *Experiments in Hearing*, McGraw-Hill, New York (1960); Description of some mechanical properties of the organ of Corti. *J. Acoust. Soc. of Am.*, 25: 4, 770-785 (1953); Shearing microphonics produced by vibrations near the inner and outer hair cells. *(id)*, 785-790 (1953).

Belanger, L. F.: Observations on the intimate structure and composition of the Chick labyrinth. *Am. J. Physiol.*, 539-545 (1961).

Brillouin, L.: *Les Tenseurs en Mécanique et en Elasticité*, Masson, Paris (1960).

Brunetti, F.: Perméabilité des membranes de l'oreille interne (avec M. Coassolo). *CR. Soc. Intern Audiol.*, Paris (1955); Effeti biologici del Rumore. *Audiotechnica News*, 1,4 (1954).

Dittrich, F. L.: De l'opportunité de quelques équations différentielles en vestibulométrie. *Experientia, 17:* 191-193 (1961); Les théories de Steinhausen et leur répercussion. *O Medico* (Lisbonne), 553: 3-10 (1962) Une nouvelle technique d'Etude des micromanipulations. *Ergonomics*, 5: 1, 285-289 (1962); Analyse des conditions physiques du stimulateur giratoire. *Confin. Neur., 21:* 390-397 (1961).

Dreyfus-Graft, J.: Phonétographe et Sub. Pormants. *Bull. Tech. PPT, 2:* 41-59 (1957); Phonétographe: Présent et Futur. *Bull. Techn. ·PTT, 5:* 160-172 (1957); Phonétographe et intelligibilité (avec. F. Dittrich) *Confin. Neurol., 21:* 468-470 (1961).

Ducrocq, A.: *Logique Générale des Systèmes et des Effets.* Dunod, Paris (1960).

Duhamel, J.: Acoustique Physique. *Cahiers de la Compagnie Française d'Audiologie.* Paris (1961).

Egger, M.: De l'audition solidienne. *CR. Soc. Neurol. Paris sc.,* Nov. 5 (1905).

Eyck, van, M.: Effets de la fatigue sur les potentiels micophoniques et nerveux du labyrinthe chez le pigeon. *Arch. Intern. Physiol., 7:* 313-320 (1950).

Faisandier, J.: *Les Mécanismes Hydrauliques.* Dunod, Paris (1957).

Feldtkeller, R.: Degrés élémentaires de la perception de la hauteur et de l'intensité (avec E. Zwicker). *Akust. Beihefte, 3:* 97-105 (1953).

Fletcher, H.: Pitch, Loudness and Quality of Musical Songs. *Am. Jour of Phys., 14:* 215-230 (1946.)

Fournier, J. E.: *L'Acoustique Musicale,* Maloine, Paris (1953).

Fulton, J. F.: *Physiologie du Système Nerveux.* Vigot, Paris (1947).

Furrer, W.: L'oreille et l'ouie, une des bases de la techniques des télécommunications. *Bull. Tech. PTT.,* 2: (1944).

Gaillard, L.: *Les Séquelles Cochléo-Vestibulaires des Traumatismes Crâniens Fermés,* Masson, Paris (1961).

Goudet, G.: *Les Fonctions de Bessel,* Mason, Paris (1954).

Gribenski, A.: *L'Audition.* P.U.F., Paris (1961.)

Groen, J. J.: A contribution to the theory of the frequency analysis mechanism in the mammalian cochlea. *Cr. Sc. Congrès Internat. ORL. Amsterdam* (1953).

Guillon, M.: *Etude et Détermination des Systèmes Hydrauliques,* Dunod, Paris (1961).

Hardung, V.: Propagation of pulse waves in visco-elastic tubing, *Handbook of Physiology,* Wilkins and W., Baltimore (1962).

Himmler, C. R.: *La Commande Hydraulique,* Dunod, Paris (1960).

Houssay, B. A.: *Physiologie Humaine,* E.M.F., Paris (1954).

Landau and Lifschitz: *Theory of Elasticity,* Pergamon Press, London (1959).

Ledoux, A.: Les canaux semi-circulaires. *Acta ORL Belgica, 12:* 113-348 (1958).

Lencastre, A.: *Manuel d'Hydraulique Générale,* Eyrolles, Paris (1961).

Massignon, D.: *Mécanique Statistique des Fluides,* Dunod, Paris (1962).

Meghigian, D.: Elletronistagmographia, *Minerva ORL,* Turin (1959).

Montandon, A.: *L'Appareil Vestibulaire et le Système Nerveux Végétatif.* Karger, New York (1946); *Les Epreuves Fonctionnelles de l'Oreille Interne,* de Vischer, Bruxelles (1956). (Other references see under Symposium.)

Montandon, P.: *Thesis,* Basle (1961).

Polonowski, M.: *Biochimie médicale,* Masson, Paris (1952).

Portmann, M.: *Précis d'Audiométrie Clinique,* Masson, Paris (1958).

Powners, R., and Lion, K. S.: Testing Eye Muscles. *Electronics, 23:* 96-99 (1950).

Quinet, J.: *Circuits de l'Electronique,* Dunod, Paris (1960).

Ranke, O. F.: *Physiologie des Zentralnervensystem,* Urban Schwartzenberg, München (1960).

Rasmussen, G. L., and Windle, W. F.: *Neural Mechanisms of the Auditory and Vestibular Systems.* Thomas, Springfield (1960).

Rauch, S.: *Einführung in die Biochemie des Höhrorgans.* Thieme, Stuttgart (1963); Biochemische Studien zum Hörvorgang. *Zeitschrift für Laryngol, 10:* 655-665 (1960).

Rocard, Y.: *Dynamique Générale des Vibrations.* Masson, Paris (1960).

Ross-Ashby, W.: *Introduction à la Cybernétique.* Dunod, Paris (1958).

Stevens, S.: *Hearing* (avec H. Davies). New York (1948).

Vallancien, B.: Sens vibratoire et audition. *Acta ORL Belgica, 1:* 61-67 (1954); La traduction de la fréquence et de l'intensité dans les voies nerveuses. *J. Franç. Orl., 3:* 309-318 (1954).

Winckel, F.: *Vues Nouvelles Sur le Monde des Sons.* Dunod, Paris (1960).

Woerdeman, H.: *Atlas d'Anatomie Humaine.* P.U.F., Paris (1956).

Zuend-Burguet, A.: *Conduction Sonore et Audition.* Maloine, Paris (1914).

Zwislocki, J.: Review of recent mathematical theories of cochlear dynamics. *J. of the Acoust. Soc. of America, 25:* 4, 743-751 (1953).

Automation, Position et Propositions. Editions Universitaires. Fribourg-en-Suisse (1957).

Ere Atomique (10 volumes). Editions R. Kisker, Genève (1959).

Symposium Otoneurologique de Bâle. *Acta ORL.,* (Stockholm) Supplementum 159.

Symposium Vestibulaire International de Genève:
    I (1954) *Practica ORL. 17:* 3, 133-235 (1955).
    II (1959) *Confin. Neurol. 20:* 3, 167-279 (1960).
    III (1961) *Confin. Neurol. 21:* 5, 357-470 (1961).

INDEX